Keep Your
Brain
Fit

THIS IS A CARLTON BOOK

This edition published in 2008 by
Carlton Books
20 Mortimer Street
London W1T 3JW

Puzzle text and content © 2000 British Mensa Limited
Introduction text, book design and artwork © 2008 Carlton Books Limited

ISBN 978-1-84732-237-1

Printed in Dubai

The puzzles in this book previously appeared in
Mensa Puzzle Challenge and *Mensa Puzzle Challenge 2*

Keep Your Brain Fit

CARLTON

WHAT IS MENSA?

Mensa is the international society for people with a high IQ.
We have more than 100,000 members in over 40 countries worldwide.

The society's aims are:
>   to identify and foster human intelligence for the benefit of humanity
>   to encourage research in the nature, characteristics, and uses of intelligence
>   to provide a stimulating intellectual and social environment for its members

Anyone with an IQ score in the top two per cent of the population is eligible to become a member of Mensa – are you the 'one in 50' we've been looking for?

Mensa membership offers an excellent range of benefits:
>   Networking and social activities nationally and around the world
>   Special Interest Groups – hundreds of chances to pursue your hobbies
>   and interests – from art to zoology!
>   Monthly members' magazine and regional newsletters
>   Local meetings – from games challenges to food and drink
>   National and international weekend gatherings and conferences
>   Intellectually stimulating lectures and seminars
>   Access to the worldwide SIGHT network for travellers and hosts

For more information about Mensa: www.mensa.org, or

British Mensa Ltd.,
St John's House,
St John's Square,
Wolverhampton
WV2 4AH
Telephone: +44 (0) 1902 772771
E-mail: enquiries@mensa.org.uk
www.mensa.org.uk

Contents

Introduction:
The Puzzle Reflex
by Tim Dedopulos

Puzzles are as old as humankind. It's inevitable – it's the way we think. Our brains make sense of the world around us by looking at the pieces that combine to make up our environment. Each piece is then compared to everything else we have encountered. We compare it by shape, size, colour, textures, a thousand different qualities, and place it into the mental categories it seems to belong to. We then also consider nearby objects, and examine what we know about them, to give context. We keep on following this web of connections until we have enough understanding of the object of our attention to allow us to proceed in the current situation. We may never have seen a larch before, but we can still identify it as a tree. Most of the time, just basic recognition is good enough, but every time we perceive an object, it is cross-referenced, analysed, pinned down – puzzled out.

This capacity for logical analysis – for reason – is one of the greatest tools in our mental arsenal, on a par with creativity and lateral induction. Without it, science would be non-existent, and mathematics no more than a shorthand for counting items. In fact, although we might have made it out of the caves, we wouldn't have got far.

Furthermore, we automatically compare ourselves to each other – we place ourselves in mental boxes along with everything else. We like to know where we stand. It gives us an instinctive urge to compete, both against our previous bests and against each other. Experience, flexibility and strength are acquired through pushing personal boundaries, and that's as true of the mind as it is of the body. Deduction is something that we derive satisfaction and worth from, part of the complex blend of factors that goes into making up our self-image. We get a very pleasurable sense of achievement from succeeding at something, particularly if we suspect it might be too hard for us.

The brain gives meaning and structure to the world through analysis, pattern recognition, and logical deduction – and our urge to measure and test ourselves is an unavoidable reflex that results from that. So what could be more natural than spending time puzzling?

EARLY PUZZLES

The urge to solve puzzles appears to be a universal human constant. They can be found in every culture, and in every era for which we have good archaeological evidence. The earliest material uncovered so far that is indisputably a puzzle has been dated to a little after 2000BC – and the first true writing we know of only dates back to 2600BC. The puzzle text is recorded on a writing tablet, preserved from ancient Babylonia. It is a mathematical puzzle based around working out the sides of a triangle.

Other puzzles from around the same time have been discovered. The Rhind Papyrus from ancient Egypt describes a puzzle that is almost certainly a precursor to the traditional English riddle "As I Was Going to St. Ives". In the Rhind Papyrus, a puzzle is constructed around the clearly unreal situation of seven houses, each containing seven cats - and every cat kills seven mice that themselves had each consumed seven ears of millet.

In a similar foreshadowing, a set of very early puzzle jugs - Phoenician work from around 1700BC, found in Cyprus - echoes designs that were to become popular in medieval Europe. These particular jugs, belonging to a broad category known as Askoi, had to be filled from the bottom. This form of trick vessel would later become known as a Cadogan Teapot. These devices have no lid, and have to be filled through a hole in the base. Because the hole funnels to a point inside the vessel, it can be filled to about half-way without spilling when it is turned back upright.

Earlier finds do exist, but so much context is lost down through the years that it can be difficult to be certain that the creators were thinking of puzzles specifically, or just of mathematical demonstrations. A set of ancient Babylonian tablets showing geometric progressions - mathematical sequences - is thought to be from 2300BC. One of the very first mathematical finds though, thought possibly to be from as far back as 2700 BC, is a set of stone balls carved into the shapes of the Platonic solids. These are regular convex polyhedrons - three-dimensional solid shapes made up solely of identical regular polygons. The most familiar is the basic cube, made up of six squares, but there are just four others - the tetrahedron, made up of four equilateral triangles; the octahedron, made up of eight equilateral triangles; the dodecahedron, made from twelve pentagons, and the icosahedron, made of twenty equilateral triangles.

There's no way now of knowing whether the carvings were teaching aids, puzzle or game tools, demonstrations of a theory, artistic constructions or even religious icons. The fact they exist at all however shows that someone had previously spent time working out a significant abstract mathematical puzzle - discovering which regular convex polyhedrons could exist.

AMENEMHET'S LABYRINTH

One of the greatest physical puzzles ever engineered comes from the same time period. The Egyptian Pharaoh Amenemhet III constructed a funerary pyramid with a huge temple complex around it in the form of an incredible labyrinth. Designed to guard the Pharaoh's mummy and treasures from disturbance or robbery, the labyrinth was so lavish and cunning that it is said to have been both the inspiration and template for the famous labyrinth that Daedalus built at Knossos for King Minos of Crete – the one that supposedly contained the Minotaur.

PUZZLE HISTORY

Coming forward in time, the evidence for the variety and complexity of puzzles gets ever stronger – an inevitable fact of archaeological and historical research. Greek legend claims that numbered dice were invented at the siege of Troy around 1200BC. We know that there was a craze for lateral thinking puzzles and logical dilemmas in the Greek culture from the 5th to 3rd centuries BC. A lot of very important mathematical work also took place in Greece from the middle of the first millennium BC, moving across to Rome during the first centuries AD. At the same time, the Chinese were playing with numerical puzzles and oddities, most famously the magic square, which they called *Lo Shu* (River Map), and also doing more strong mathematical work.

Puzzles and puzzle-like games that survive through to modern times get more common as we get closer to modern times, naturally. The game of Go arose in China some time around 500 BC, spreading to Japan a thousand years later – it is still an important sport there. At the same time, Chess was first appearing, either in India (*Chaturanga*), China (*Xiang-qi*), or both. Puzzle rings that you have to work out how to separate also appeared in China, possibly in the 3rd century AD, as did Snakes & Ladders, around 700AD.

The first known reference to a game played with cards is in 969AD, in records reporting the activities of the Chinese Emperor Mu-tsung. These are not thought to be the playing cards now familiar in the west, however – it seems likely that those arose in Persia during the 11th or 12th century AD. The physical puzzle Solitaire is first reported in 1697AD. As the eighteenth century gave way to the nineteenth, the forces of the industrial revolution really started to transform the way that ideas propagated, and the puzzle world exploded. Some of the more notable highlights include the invention of the jigsaw puzzle by John Spilsbury in 1767; Tic-Tac-Toe's first formal discussion in 1820, by Charles Babbage; poker first appearing around 1830 in the USA; Lucas inventing the Tower of Hanoi puzzle in 1883; the first crossword appearing in New York World on December 21, 1913, created by Arthur Wynne; Erno Rubik's invention of his Cube in 1974; and the invention of Sudoku in 1979 for Dell Magazines by Howard Garns, an American, who first called it "Number Place".

PLASTICITY

It turns out that it's a good thing puzzles are such an important part of the human psyche. Recent advances in the scientific fields of neurology and cognitive psychology have hammered home the significance of puzzles and mental exercise like never before.

We now understand that the brain continually builds, shapes and organises itself all through our lives. It is the only organ able to do so. Previously, we had assumed that the brain was constructed to optimise infant development, but the truth is that it continually rewrites its own operating instructions. It can route around physical damage, maximise its efficiency in dealing with commonly encountered situations and procedures, and alter its very structure in response to our experiences. This incredible flexibility is referred to as plasticity.

The most important implication of plasticity is that our mental abilities and cognitive fitness can be exercised at any age. Just like the muscles of the body, our minds can respond to exercise, allowing us to be more retentive and mentally fitter. Our early lives are the most important time, of course. Infants develop almost twice as many synapses – the mental connections that are the building-blocks of the mind – as we retain as adults, to make sure that every experience can be learnt from and given its own space in the developing mental structure. The first thirty-six months are particularly vital, the ones which will shape the patterns of our intellect, character and socialisation for life. A good education through to adulthood – stretching the brain right through childhood – is one of the strongest indicators of late-life mental health, particularly when followed with a mentally challenging working life.

Just as importantly however, there is little difference between the brain at the age of 25 and the age of 75. As time passes, the brain optimises itself for the lifestyle we feed it. Circuits that are hardly ever used get re-adapted to offer greater efficiency in tasks we regularly use. Just as our body maximises available energy by removing muscle we don't use, the brain removes mental tone we're never stretching – and in the same way that working out can build up muscle, so mental exercise can restore a "fit" mind.

PUZZLE SOLVING AND BRAIN GROWTH

A surprising amount of mental decline in elders is now thought to be down to insufficient mental exercise. Where severe mental decline occurs, it is usually linked to the tissue damage of Alzheimer's Disease – although there is now evidence that strong mental exercise lets the brain route around even Alzheimer's damage, lessening impairment. In other cases, where there is no organic damage, the main cause is disuse. Despite old assumptions, we do not significantly lose huge swathes of brain cells as we age. Better still, mental strength that has been allowed to atrophy may be rebuilt.

Research projects across the world have discovered strong patterns linking highly lucid venerable people. These include above-average education, acceptance of change, satisfying personal accomplishments, physical exercise, a clever spouse, and a strong engagement with life, including reading, social activity, travel, keeping up with new ideas, and regularly solving puzzles. Not all the things we assume to be engagement are actually helpful, however. Useful intellectual pursuits are the actively stimulating ones – such as solving jigsaws, crosswords and other puzzles, playing chess, and reading books that stimulate the imagination or require some mental effort to properly digest. However, passive intellectual pursuits may actually hasten the mind's decay. Watching television is the most damaging such pastime, but surprisingly anything that makes you "switch off" mentally can also be harmful, such as listening to certain types of music, reading very low-content magazines and even getting most of your social exposure on the telephone. For social interaction to be helpful, it may really need to be face to face.

THE COLUMBIA STUDY

A team of researchers from Columbia University in New York tracked more than 1,750 pensioners from the northern Manhattan region over a period of seven years. The subjects underwent periodic medical and psychological examination to assess both their mental health and the physical condition of their brains. Participants also provided the researchers with detailed information regarding their daily activities. The study found that even when you remove education and career attainment from the equation, leisure activity significantly reduced the risk of dementia.

The study's author, Dr Yaakov Stern, found that "Even when controlling for factors like ethnic group, education and occupation, subjects with high leisure activity had 38% less risk of developing dementia." Activities were broken into three categories: physical, social and intellectual. Each one was found to be beneficial, but the greatest protection came from intellectual pursuits. The more activity, the greater the protection – the cumulative benefit of each separate leisure pursuit was found to be 8%. Stern also found that leisure activity helped to prevent the physical damage caused by Alzheimer's from actually manifesting as dementia:

> "Our study suggests that aspects of life experience supply a set of skills or repertoires that allow an individual to cope with progressing Alzheimer's Disease pathology for a longer time before the disease becomes clinically apparent. Maintaining intellectual and social engagement through participation in everyday activities seems to buffer healthy individuals against cognitive decline in later life."

STAYING LUCID

There is strong evidence to back Stern's conclusion. Dr David Bennett of the Rush Alzheimer's Disease Centre in Chicago led a study that evaluated a group of elderly participants on a yearly basis, and then after death examined their donated brains for signs of Alzheimer's. The participants all led active lives mentally, socially and physically, and none of them suffered from dementia at the time of their death. It was discovered that more than a third of the participants had sufficient brain-tissue damage to warrant diagnosis of Alzheimer's Disease, including serious lesions in the brain tissue. This group *had* recorded lower scores than other participants in episodic memory tests – remembering story episodes, for example – but performed identically in cognitive function and reasoning tests. A similar study took place with the aid of the nuns of the Order of the School Sisters of Notre Dame. The Order boasts a long average lifespan – 85 years – and came to the attention of researchers when it became clear that its members did not seem to suffer from any dementia either. The distinguishing key about the Order is that the nuns shun idleness and mental vacuity, taking particular effort to remain mentally active. All sorts of pursuits are encouraged, such as solving puzzles, playing challenging games, writing, holding seminars on current affairs, knitting and engaging with local government. As before, there was plenty of evidence of the physical damage associated with Alzheimer's Disease, but none of the mental damage that usually accompanied it, even in some nonagenarian participants.

MENTAL REPAIR

Other studies have also tried to enumerate the benefits of mental activity. A massive group study led by Michael Valenzuela from the University of New South Wales' School of Psychiatry tracked data from almost 30,000 people worldwide. The results were clear – as well as indicating the same clear relationship previously found between schooling, career and mental health, people of all backgrounds whose daily lives include a high degree of mental stimulation are 46% less likely to suffer dementia. This holds true even for people who take up mentally challenging activities as they get older – if you use your mind, the brain still adapts to protect it. If you do not use it, the brain lets it falter.

PUZZLE SOLVING TECHNIQUES

Puzzle solving is more of an art than a science. It requires mental flexibility, a little understanding of the underlying principles and possibilities, and sometimes a little intuition. It is often said of crosswords that you have to learn the writer's style to get really good at his or her puzzles, but the same thing applies to most other puzzle types to a certain extent, and that includes the many and various kinds you'll find in this book.

SEQUENCE PUZZLES

Sequence puzzles challenge you to find a missing value or item, or to complete a pattern according to the correct underlying design. In this type of puzzle, you are provided with enough previous entries in the sequence that the underlying logic can be worked out. Once the sequence is understood, the missing entry can be calculated. When the patterns are simple, the sequence will be readily visible to the naked eye. It is not hard to figure out that the next term in the sequence 1, 2, 4, 8, 16, ? is going to be a further doubling to 32. Numerical sequences are just the expression of a mathematical formula however, and can therefore get almost infinitely complex.

Proper recreational puzzles stay firmly within the bounds of human ability, of course. With the more complex puzzles, the best approach is often to calculate the differences between successive terms in the sequences, and look for patterns in the way that those differences are changing. You should also be aware that in some puzzles, the terms of a sequence may not necessarily represent single items. Different parts or digits of each term may progress according to different calculations. For example, the sequence 921, 642, 383, 164 is actually three simple sequences stuck together - 9, 6, 2, 0 ; 2, 4, 8, 16; and 1, 2, 3, 4. The next term will be - 3325. Alternatively, in puzzles where the sequence terms are given as times, they may actually just represent the times they depict, but they might also be literal numbers, or pairs of numbers to be treated as totally different sequences, or even require conversion from hours: minutes to just minutes before the sequence becomes apparent.

For example, 11:14 in a puzzle might represent the time 11:14, or perhaps the time 23:14 - or the numbers 11 and 14, the numbers 23 and 14, the number 1114, the number 2314, or even the number 674 (11 * 60 minutes, with the remaining 14 minutes also added). As you can see, solving sequence puzzles requires a certain amount of trial and error as you test difference possibilities, as well as a degree of lateral thinking. It would be a very harsh puzzle setter who expected you to guess some sort of sequence out of context however. So in the absence of a clue

otherwise, 11:14 would be highly unlikely to represent 11 months and 14 days, or the value 11 in base 14, or even 11 hours and 14 minutes converted to seconds - unless it was given as 11:14:00, of course.

Letter-based sequences are all representational of course, as unlike numbers, letters have no underlying structure save as symbols. Once you deduce what the letters represent, the answer can be obvious. The sequence D, N, O, ? may seem abstract, until you think of months of the year in reverse order.

In visual sequences - such as pattern grids - the sequence will always be there for you to see, and your task is to look for repeating patterns. As with number sequences, easy grids can be immediately apparent. In harder puzzles, the sequences can become significantly long, and often be presented in ways that make them difficult to identify. Puzzle setters love to start grids of this type from the bottom right-hand square, and then progress in spirals or in a back-and-forth pattern - sometimes even diagonally.

Odd-one-out problems are a specialised case of sequence pattern where you are given the elements of a sequence or related set, along with one item that breaks the sequence. Like other sequence puzzles, these can range from very easy to the near-impossible. Spotting the odd one in 2, 4, 6, 7, 8 is trivial. It would be almost impossible to guess the odd item from the set B, F, H,

N, O unless you already knew that the set in question was the physical elements on the second row of the standard periodic table. Even then, you might need a copy of the periodic table itself to notice that hydrogen, H, is on the first row. As with any other sequence problem, any odd-one-out should contain enough information in the puzzle, accompanying text and title to set the context for finding the correct answer. In the above case, a puzzle title along the lines of "An Elementary Puzzle" would probably be sufficient to make it fair game.

EQUATION PUZZLES

Equation puzzles are similar to sequences, but require a slightly different methodology. In these problems, you are given a set of mathematical calculations that contain one or more unknown terms. These may be represented as equations, as in the traditional form of $2x + 3y = 9$, or they may be presented visually, for example as two anvils and three iron bars on one side of a scale and nine horseshoes balancing on the other side of the scale. For each Unknown – x, y, anvils, etc – you need one equation or other set of values before you can calculate a definitive answer. If these are lacking, you cannot get the problem down to just one possible solution. Take the equation above, $2x + 3y = 9$. There are two unknowns, and therefore many

answers. For example, x can be 3 and y can be 1 – for x, 2 * 3 = 6; for y, 3 * 1 = 3, and overall, 6 + 3 = 9 – but x can also be 1.5 and y can be 2… and an infinite range of other possibilities. So when solving equation puzzles, you need to consider all the equations together before you can solve the problem.

To return to our example equation above, if you *also* knew that $x + 2y = 7$, you could then begin to solve the puzzle. The key with equation problems is to get your equation down to containing just one unknown term, which then lets you get a value for that term, and in turn lets you get the value of the other unknown/s. So, for example, in our previous equations ($2x + 3y = 9$ and $x + 2y = 7$) you could manipulate one equation to work out what x actually represents in terms of y ("How many Y is each X?") in one equation, and then replace the x in the other equation with it's value in y, to get a calculation that just has y as the sole unknown factor. It's not as confusing as it sounds so long as you take it step by step:

We know that

$x + 2y = 7$

Any change made to both sides of an equation balances out, and so doesn't change the truth of the equation. For example, consider 2 + 2 = 4. If you add 1 to each side, the equation is still true. That is, 2 + 2 + 1 = 4 + 1. We can use this cancelling out to get x and y on opposite sides of the equation, which will let us represent x in terms of y:

x + 2y - 2y = 7 - 2y.

Now the + 2y - 2y cancels out:

x = 7 - 2y.

Now we know x is a way of saying "7-2y", we can replace it in the other equation.

2x + 3y = 9 becomes:

2 * (7 - 2y) + 3y = 9.

Note 2x means that x is in the equation twice, so our way of re-writing x as y needs to be doubled to stay accurate.

Expanding that out:

(2 * 7) - (2 * 2y) + 3y = 9, or

14 - 4y + 3y = 9.

The next step is to get just amounts of y on one side, and numbers on the other.

14 - 4y + 3y - 14 = 9 - 14.

In other words,

-4y + 3y = -5.

Now, -4 + 3 is -1, so:

-y = -5, and that means y=5.

Now you can go back to the first equation, x + 2y = 7, and replace y to find x.

x + (2 * 5) = 7

x + 10 = 7

x + 10 - 10 = 7 - 10

x = 7 - 10

and, finally.

x = -3.

As a last step, test your equations by replacing your number values for x and y in both at the same time, and making sure they balance correctly.

2x + 3y = 9 and x + 2y = 7.

(2 * -3) + (3 * 5) = 9 and -3 + (2 * 5) = 7

(-6 + 15) = 9; and (-3 + 10) = 7.

9 = 9 and 7 = 7.

The answers are correct.

Any equation-based puzzle you're presented with will contain enough information for you to work out the solution. If more than two terms are unknown, the technique is to use one equation to find one unknown as a value of the others, and then replace it in all the other equations. That gives you a new set of equations containing one less unknown term. You then repeat the process of working out an unknown again, until you finally get down to one unknown term and its numerical value. Then you replace the term you now know with its value in the equations for the level above to get the next term, and continue back on up like that. It's like a mathematical version of the old wooden Towers of Hanoi puzzle. As a final tip, remember that you should have one equation per unknown term, and that if one of your unknown variables is missing from an equation, the equation can be said to have 0 of that variable on either or both sides. That is, 4y + 2z = 8 is the same as 0x + 4y + 2z = 8.

Happy puzzling!

REFERENCES

Chronology of Recreational Mathematics; David Singmaster; http://www.eldar.org/~problemi/singmast/recchron.html

Pythagoras's theorem in Babylonian mathematics; J J O'Connor and E F Robertson; http://www-history.mcs.st-andrews.ac.uk/HistTopics/Babylonian_Pythagoras.html

The Rhind Mathematical Papyrus; http://en.wikipedia.org/wiki/Rhind_Mathematical_Papyrus

Puzzle Jug; http://en.wikipedia.org/wiki/Puzzle_jug

The Egyptian Labyrinth; http://www.amazeingart.com/seven-wonders/egyptian-labyrinth.html

The Ancient Egyptian Labyrinth; http://www.catchpenny.org/labyrin.html

Alzheimer's: Prevention, Treatment, and Slowing Down; Doug Russell, Jeanne Segal and Monika White; http://www.helpguide.org/elder/alzheimers_prevention_slowing_down_treatment.htm

The Human Brain; http://www.fi.edu/brain/exercise.htm

Power Up Your Brain; Terri Needels & Toby Bilanow; http://health.msn.com/guides/agingwell/articlepage.aspx?cp-documentid=100143902

Keeping Your Brain Fit For Life; Katherine Kam; http://www.positscience.com/newsroom/news/news/111406.php

Preliminary Results from PopCap Games and Games for Health; Peter Smith; http://www.gamesforhealth.org/archives/000125.html

Older Game Players Derive Mental Workouts, Stress Relief and Pain Distraction from Playing; Garth Chouteau; http://www.popcap.com/press/index.php?page=press_releases&release=survey_seniors_10-4-06

Complex Brain Circuits May Protect Against Alzheimer's; Susan Conova; http://www.cumc.columbia.edu/news/in-vivo/Vol3_Iss11_nov_dec_04/index.html

Use It or Lose It?; Beth Azar; http://www.apa.org/monitor/may02/useit.html

Fight Alzheimer's With an Active Brain; http://www.msnbc.msn.com/id/8292945

Want a Sharp Mind for your Golden Years? Start Now; Marilyn Elias; http://www.bri.ucla.edu/bri_weekly/news_050818.asp

How to Prevent Alzheimer's; http://www.sixwise.com/newsletters/05/08/24/how_to_prevent_alzheimers_the_most_effective_ways_to_avoid_this_rapidly_increasing_disease.htm

Lifestyle May Be Key to Slowing Brain's Aging; Rob Stein; http://www.washingtonpost.com/wp-dyn/content/article/2005/08/13/AR2005081300855.html

Disorder May Precede Alzheimer's; John Fauber; http://www.findarticles.com/p/articles/mi_qn4196/is_20050308/ai_n12411071

Mental Activities May Reduce Alzheimer's Risk; http://www.kirotv.com/health/1232090/detail.html

Brain Savers; A. J. Mann; http://www.time.com/time/magazine/article/0,9171,1002535,00.html?internalid=ACA

Building a Better Brain; Daniel Golden & Alexander Tsiaras; http://www.enchantedmind.com/html/science/build_better_brain.html

The Nuns Who Won't Sit Still; Marge Engelmann; http://www.agenet.com/Category_Pages/document_display.asp?Id=12561&

Mental Exercise Nearly Halves Risk of Dementia; http://www.livescience.com/humanbiology/060125_delay_dementia.html

Use Your Brain, Halve Your Risk of Dementia; Susi Hamilton; http://www.unsw.edu.au/news/pad/articles/2006/jan/Dementia_brain_reserve.html

14-Day Health Plan Improves Memory; http://www.livescience.com/humanbiology/051213_memory_exercise.html

The Happiness Manifesto; http://www.uofapain.med.ualberta.ca/documents/manifesto1.pdf

Can We Live Happily Ever After?; Ron Horvath; http://www.australianreview.net/digest/2006/10/horvath.html

Simple Lifestyle Changes May Improve Cognitive Function; http://www.news-medical.net/?id=18102

Effects of Self-Esteem on Age-Related Changes in Cognition; Sonia Lupien, Jens Pruessner, Catherine Lord and Michael Meaney; http://www.annalsnyas.org/cgi/content/full/1032/1/186

Low Self-Esteem 'Shrinks Brain'; Pallab Ghosh; http://news.bbc.co.uk/2/hi/health/3224674.stm

Easy Puzzles

If solving puzzles is a pleasurable activity – and all the evidence that we have suggests that it most certainly is – then this is the section that will let you sharpen your knife in preparation for the feast. The puzzles here represent the same types of problem that you'll find throughout this book. They'll certainly get you thinking, but not too hard – the answers to these problems are reassuringly straightforward, and you may find that many of them are readily apparent.

Don't get complacent, however. As well as warming up your mind for the challenges to come, this section also gives you an important chance to get used to the way that the puzzles work. You'll start to get a feeling for the way that the puzzle authors are thinking, and you'll also pick up a good intuitive grounding in the particular vagaries of the different puzzle types.

If you're new to puzzles, then it's probably going to be best for you to work your way through this entire section before moving on to the next one. Get a firm victory under your belt – and remember to pat yourself on the back – before moving on to some of the harsher problems. If you're more experienced in the ways of puzzling, you might prefer to dip into this section to warm yourself up, starting each of your puzzle sessions with a few of the problems here to get your brain in gear.

Whichever way you approach these problems however, remember one critical thing – to have fun!

PUZZLE 1

Each shape in this diagram has a value. Work out the values to discover what numbers should replace the question marks.

Answer see page **102**

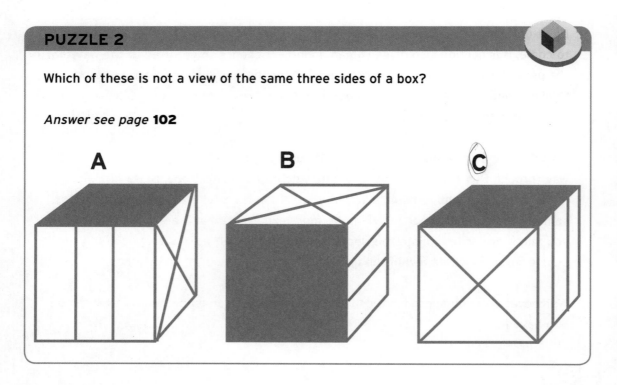

PUZZLE 2

Which of these is not a view of the same three sides of a box?

Answer see page **102**

A

B

C

PUZZLE 3

Each shape in the diagram has a value. Work out the values to discover what number should replace the question mark.

Answer see page **102**

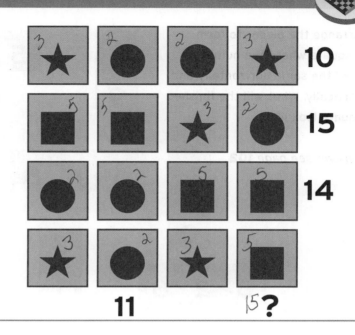

PUZZLE 4

There is only one way to open this safe. You must press each button once only, in the correct order, to reach OPEN. Each button is marked with a direction, U for up, L for left, D for down, R for right. The number of spaces to move is also marked on each button. Which button must you press first to open the safe?

Answer see page **102**

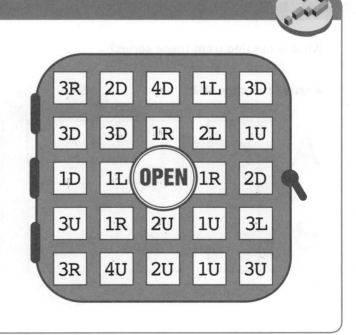

PUZZLE 5

Arrange the pieces to form a square where the numbers read the same horizontally and vertically. What will the finished square look like?

Answer see page **102**

8
9

5 1

0
1

4
6
0

2
4
7

1 4 8

2 4

5 2 6

3
1

7 3 1

PUZZLE 6

What is missing from these series?

Answer see page **102**

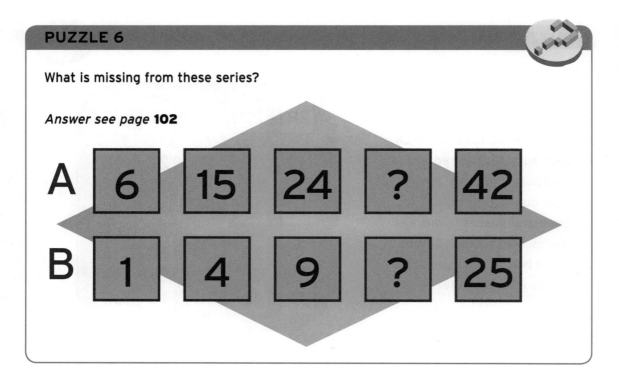

A   6   15   24   ?   42

B   1   4   9   ?   25

PUZZLE 7

Should A, B, C or D come next in the series?

Answer see page **102**

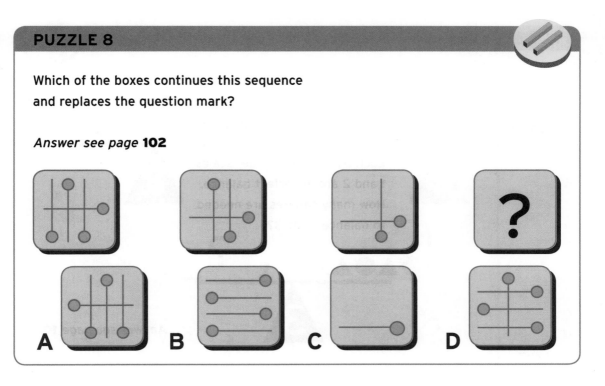

A   B   C   D

PUZZLE 8

Which of the boxes continues this sequence
and replaces the question mark?

Answer see page **102**

A   B   C   D

PUZZLE 9

2   **5**   **11**

3   **?**

What number is missing from this series?

Answer see page **102**

PUZZLE 10

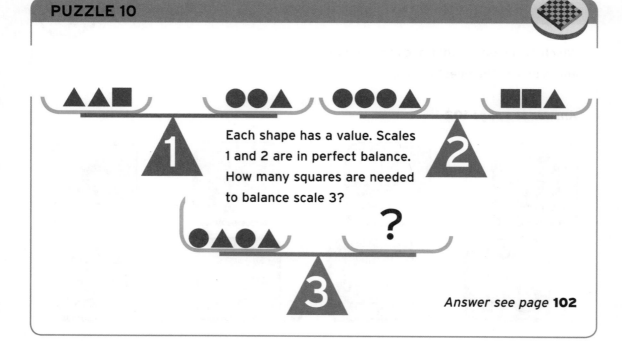

Each shape has a value. Scales 1 and 2 are in perfect balance. How many squares are needed to balance scale 3?

Answer see page **102**

Which two boxes in this diagram are similar?

A B C D

Answer see page **102**

PUZZLE 12

Which of these discs is the odd one out?

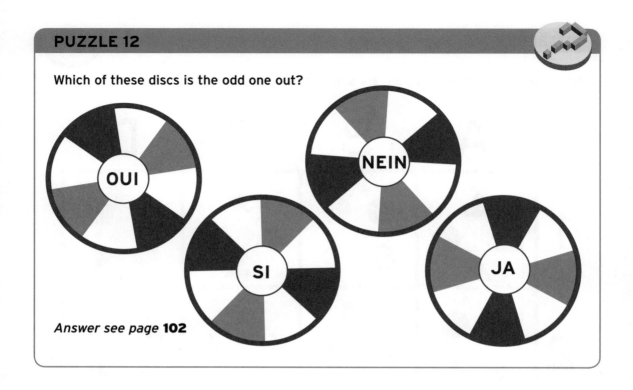

Answer see page **102**

PUZZLE 13

Which two boxes are similar?

Answer see page **102**

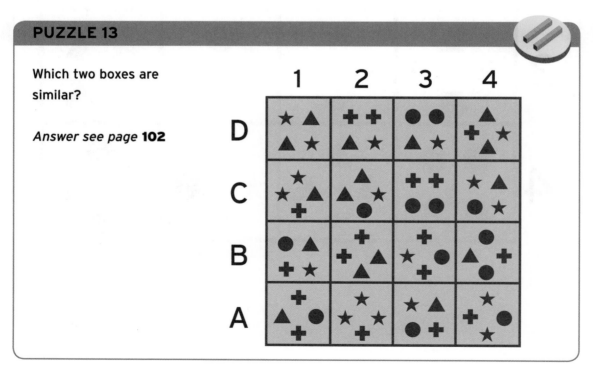

PUZZLE 14

Each same symbol in the diagram has the same value – one of which is a negative number. Can you work out the logic and discover which number should replace the question mark and the values of the symbols?

Answer see page **102**

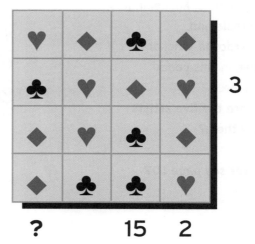

3

? 15 2

PUZZLE 15

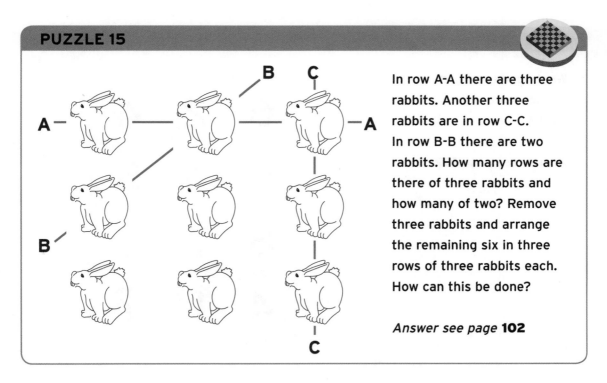

In row A-A there are three rabbits. Another three rabbits are in row C-C. In row B-B there are two rabbits. How many rows are there of three rabbits and how many of two? Remove three rabbits and arrange the remaining six in three rows of three rabbits each. How can this be done?

Answer see page **102**

PUZZLE 16

Three artists, Michelangelo, Constable and Leonardo Da Vinci are hidden in this coded message.
Who are the five artists below them?

Answer see page **102**

1
2
3
4
5
6

PUZZLE 17

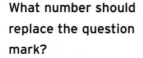

What number should replace the question mark?

Answer see page **102**

6	2	4
9	4	5
8	7	1
4	1	?

PUZZLE 18

The minute and hour hands move separately on these strange clocks. What time should the fourth clock show?

Answer see page **102**

1   **2**   **3**   **4**

PUZZLE 19

Move from square to touching square, including diagonals, to discover the longest possible country name from these letters.

Answer see page **103**

Z	E	D	N
W	T	R	A
I	S	L	P

PUZZLE 20

N	B	W	R	Y	A	V	M	D	A
X	E	J	V	D	H	A	O	I	C
H	B	W	A	C	R	K	N	A	F
Y	D	V	M	I	T	R	T	K	G
K	E	F	Z	E	O	W	A	S	N
N	Q	O	X	F	X	Q	N	A	I
B	N	A	I	G	P	I	A	L	M
A	S	L	H	C	B	F	C	A	O
P	A	J	N	O	G	E	R	O	Y
C	O	L	O	R	A	D	O	G	W

In the grid find all the American States listed below.

Alaska   California
Montana   New Mexico
Texas   Arizona
Colorado   Nevada
Oregon   Wyoming

Answer see page **103**

PUZZLE 21

5A   4E   2B   1E   1C   4D   5C   1B   4B

☐ ☐ ☐ ☐ ☐ ☐ ☐ ☐ ☐ ☐

1D   3D   1E   1C   1B   3A   4C   4E   1E

The wordframe above, when filled with the correct letters, gives the name of a famous boxer. However, to make things interesting you have to decide which letters from the grid (right) are correct.

Answer see page **103**

	A	B	C	D	E
1	G	R	T	J	E
2	P	K	C	B	W
3	Y	X	F	I	H
4	U	N	Z	A	O
5	M	D	S	V	L

PUZZLE 22

Arrange these pieces to form a square where the numbers read the same horizontally and vertically. What will the finished square look like?

```
8 6 4          4 7 6

3   0     3    3   1   7
8   8     5    3   5   6
    5                4
    2 6   5
          2
          0
```

Answer see page 103

PUZZLE 23

Start at the far left circle and move along the lines to the far right circle, collecting the numbers, the diamonds and the ovals as you go. Each oval has a value of minus 10. Each diamond has a value of minus 15.
What are the minimum and maximum totals possible?

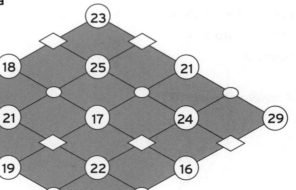

Answer see page 103

PUZZLE 24

The wordframe below, when filled with the correct letters, will give the name of a composer. The letters are arranged in the coded square. There are two possible letters to fill each square of the wordframe, one correct, the other is incorrect each time. Who is the composer?

Answer see page **103**

	A	B	C	D	E
1	W	T	E	D	E
2	F	C	R	H	P
3	E	U	A	I	U
4	K	M	B	V	S
5	O	L	J	G	N

4C	1E	5B	1B	3C	4B	3E	1C	4A
1A	3D	3A	4E	2D	5A	4D	2B	5E

PUZZLE 25

The codes for these letters are shown below. Who are these famous historical scientists?

Answer see page **103**

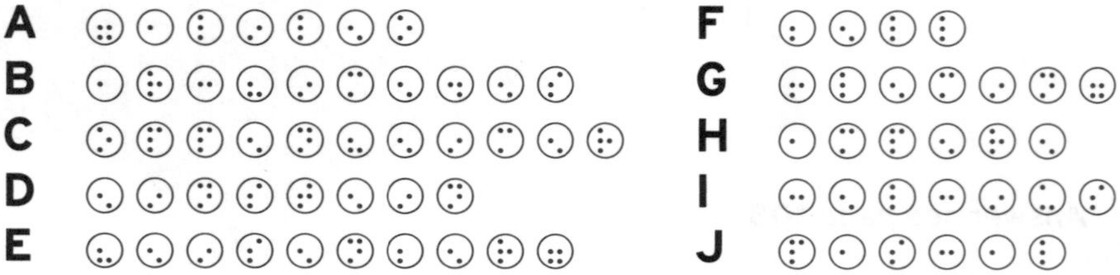

A B C D E F

G H I L M N

O P R S T U

A
B
C
D
E

F
G
H
I
J

PUZZLE 26

Starting from the top left corner, follow the symbols in a continuous down and up route. Which direction, north, south, east or west, should go in the empty space?

Answer see page **103**

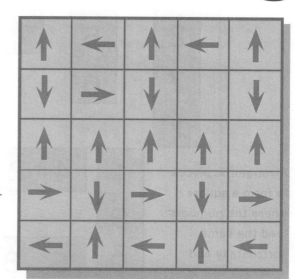

PUZZLE 27

This is an unusual safe. To open it you must press the OPEN button, but you must press all the other buttons in the correct order. This can only be done by following the directions and the number of steps to be taken. Which is the first button you should push?

4R	4D	3D	3L	4D
2D	1D	1U	1L	1D
3R	2U	2L	2D	2L
4R	2U	1L	2U	2U
3U	1R	2L	4U	OPEN

Answer see page **103**

PUZZLE 28

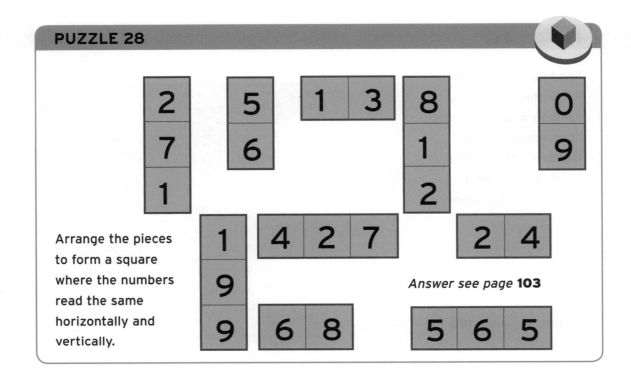

Arrange the pieces to form a square where the numbers read the same horizontally and vertically.

Answer see page **103**

PUZZLE 29

Which one of the following numbers is the odd one out?

Answer see page **103**

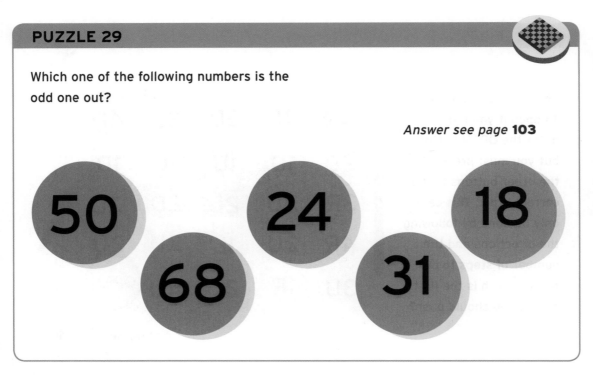

PUZZLE 30

Arrange the pieces to form a square where the numbers read the same horizontally and vertically. What will the finished square look like?

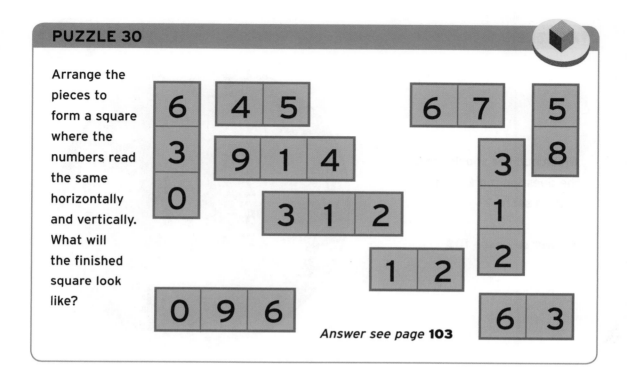

Answer see page **103**

PUZZLE 31

In her piggy bank, Jane has $5.24. The sum is made up of an equal number of four coins from 1¢, 5¢, 10¢, 25¢, 50¢ and $1, Which four coins does she have and how many of each of them?

Answer see page 103

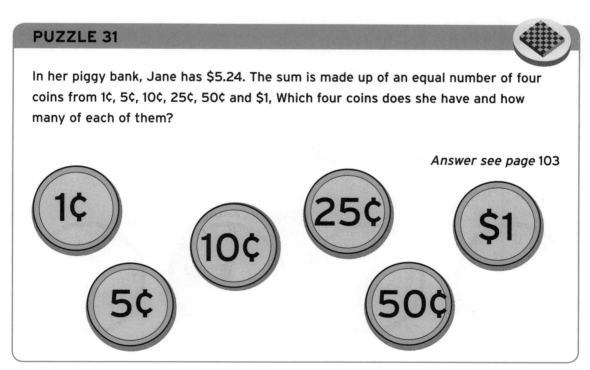

PUZZLE 32

Which number should replace the question mark in the bottom sector?

Answer see page **103**

5 4
7 6
3 5
8 7
11 2 4 5
7 5 8 2
4 6
2 6
3 11
? 3

PUZZLE 33

The hands on these clocks move in a strange but logical way. What is the time on the fourth clock?

Answer see page **103**

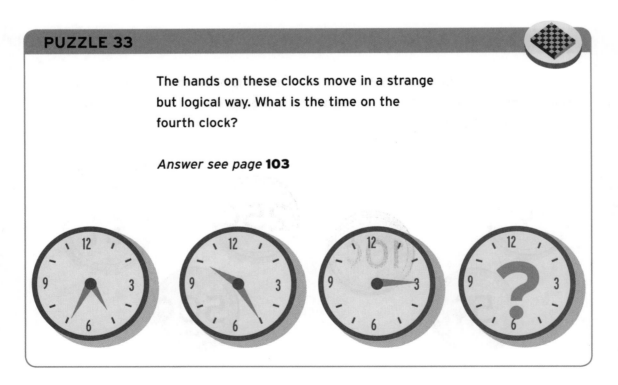

PUZZLE 34

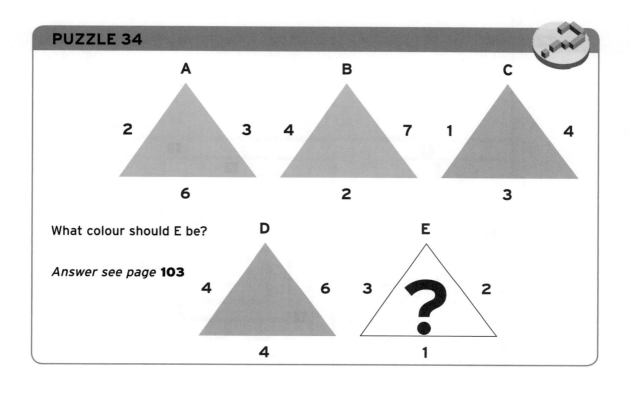

A
2   3
6

B
4   7
2

C
1   4
3

What colour should E be?

Answer see page **103**

D
4   6
4

E
3   **?**   2
1

PUZZLE 35

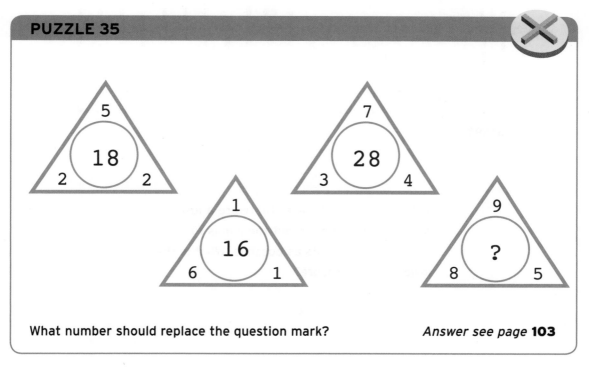

5
18
2   2

7
28
3   4

1
16
6   1

9
?
8   5

What number should replace the question mark?

Answer see page **103**

FINISH

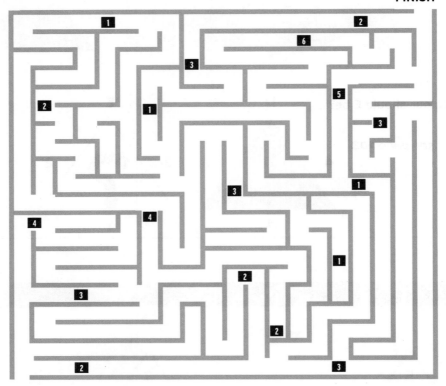

START

This is an unusual maze. There are a few
ways of completing it, but the aim is to
collect as few points as possible. What is the
lowest possible score?

Answer see page **104**

Which of these is not a view of the same box?

Answer see page **104**

A

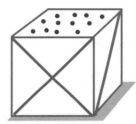

B

C

D

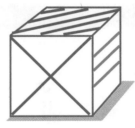

E

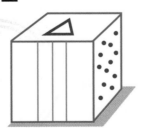

F

PUZZLE 38

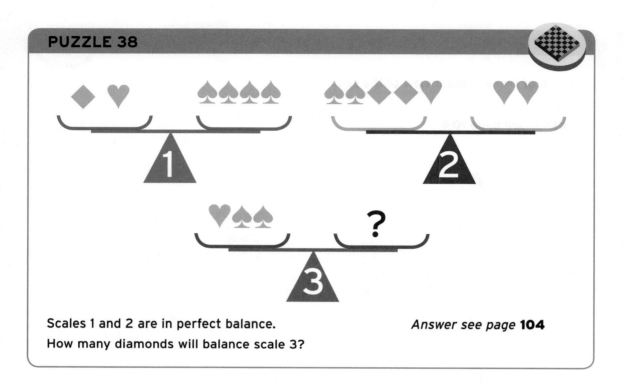

Scales 1 and 2 are in perfect balance.
How many diamonds will balance scale 3?

Answer see page **104**

PUZZLE 39

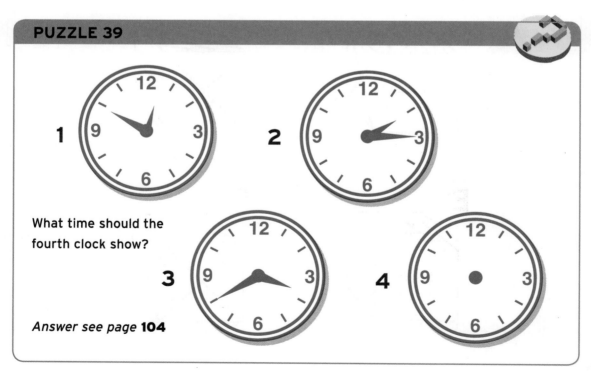

What time should the
fourth clock show?

Answer see page **104**

The hands on these clocks move in a strange but logical way. What time should replace the question mark?

Answer see page **104**

Each same symbol has the same value in this grid. Which number replaces the question mark and what are their values?

Answer see page **104**

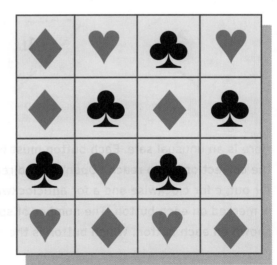

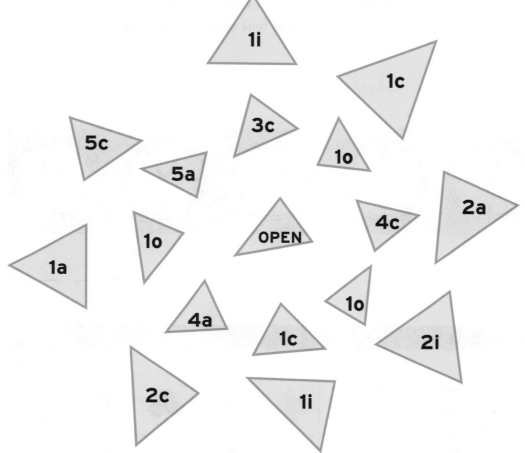

Here is an unusual safe. Each button must be pressed once only, in the correct order, to reach "Open". The direction to move, i for in, o for out, c for clockwise and a for anticlockwise (or counterclockwise) is marked on each button. The number of spaces to move is also shown on each button. Which button is the first you must press?

Answer see page **104**

PUZZLE 43

The minute and hour hands are moving
separately on these weird clocks. What time
will the fourth clock show?

Answer see page **104**

PUZZLE 44

Start at the far left circle and move along the lines to the far right circle,
collecting the numbers and shapes as you go. Each oval means divide by 2,
each square means multiply by 3, and each triangle means add 13. What are
the maximum and minimum totals possible?

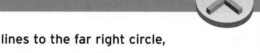

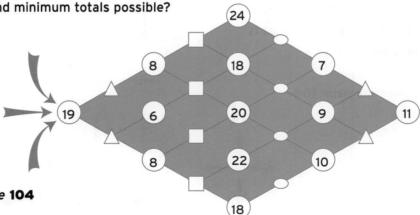

Answer see page **104**

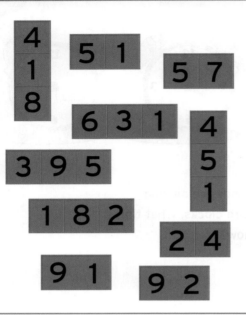

Arrange the pieces to form a square where the numbers read the same vertically and horizontally. What will the finished square look like?

Answer see page **104**

The arrows from this grid go from the top left corner in a logical sequence. In which direction should the arrow go in the empty box and what is the order?

Answer see page **104**

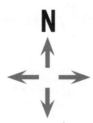

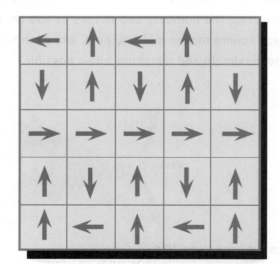

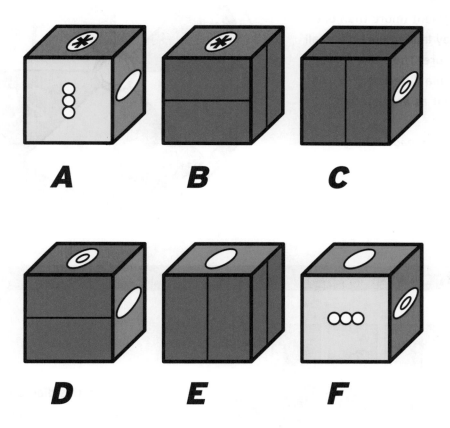

Which of these is not a view
of the same box?

Answer see page **104**

PUZZLE 48

On this unusual dartboard how many different ways are there to score 30 with three darts? Every dart must land in a segment (more than one dart may land in each), and all must score. The same three scores in a different order do not count as another way.

Answer see page **104**

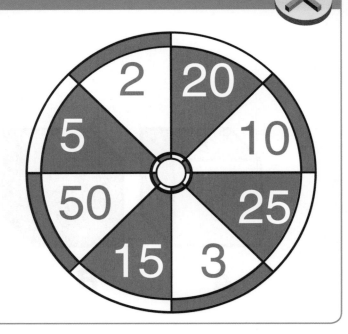

PUZZLE 49

    ?

    22

    25

    25

26

Each shape in this diagram has a value. Work out the values to discover what number should replace the question mark.

Answer see page **104**

PUZZLE 50

Each shape in the diagram has a value. Work out the values to discover what number should replace the question mark.

Answer see page **104**

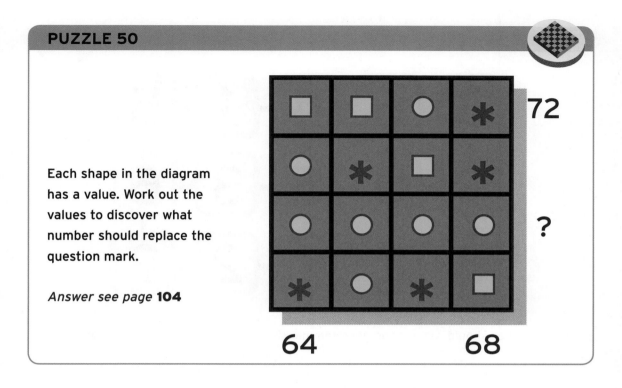

PUZZLE 51

Should A, B, C or D come next in this series?

Answer see page **104**

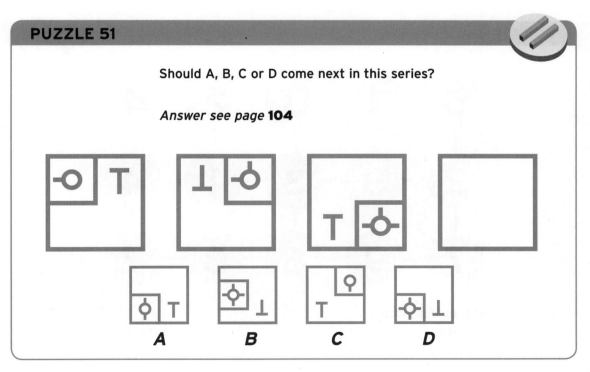

A   B   C   D

3 6 4 1 5
9 8 5 3 6
6 2 1 2 ?

What number should replace the question mark?

Answer see page **104**

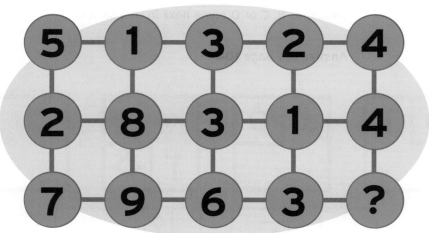

5 1 3 2 4
2 8 3 1 4
7 9 6 3 ?

What number should replace
the question mark?

Answer see page **104**

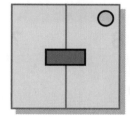 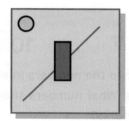 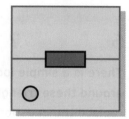 

Which box follows the
shapes in the first three
boxes?

Answer see page **104**

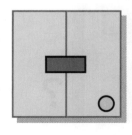 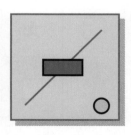 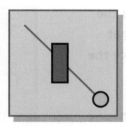 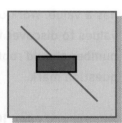

A   **B**   **C**   **D**

PUZZLE 55

1
5
5   6

2
6
6   ?

3
7
7   10

4
?
8   ?

There is a simple logic to the numbers in and around these triangles. What numbers should replace the question marks?

Answer see page **105**

PUZZLE 56

Each shape in the diagram has a value. Work out the values to discover what number should replace the question mark.

Answer see page **105**

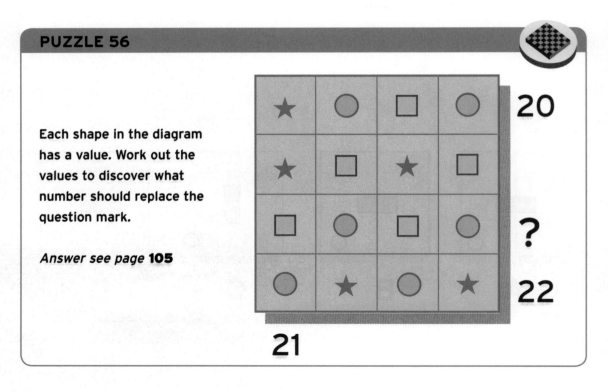

20

?

22

21

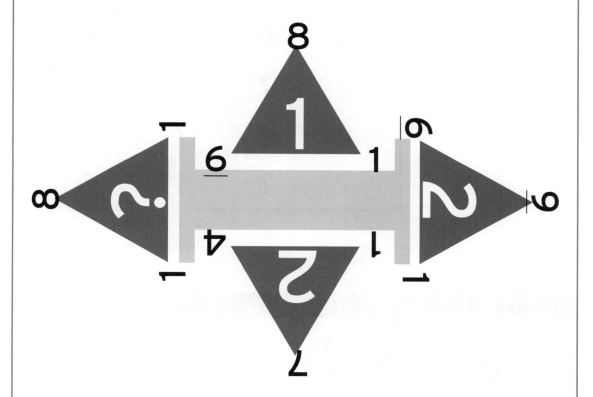

What number should replace the question mark in the fourth triangle?

Answer see page **105**

What two digits will
replace the question
marks?

Answer see page **105**

7	8	5	3
5	0	6	4
2	7	8	9
2	2	7	5
?	?	1	4

8	1	2	4
6	1	3	7
9	1	7	8
5	1	4	9
8	?	?	8

What number should replace
the question mark?

Answer see page **105**

PUZZLE 60

Which of the numbers on these balloons is the odd one out?

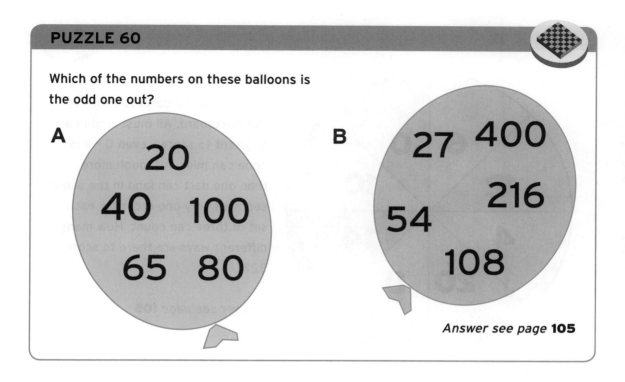

A

20
40 100
65 80

B

27 400
216
54
108

Answer see page **105**

PUZZLE 61

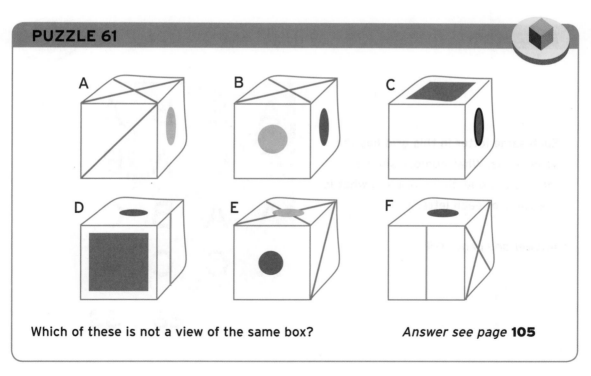

A

B

C

D

E

F

Which of these is not a view of the same box?

Answer see page **105**

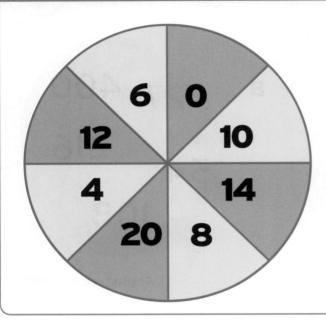

You have three darts to throw at this dartboard. All must land in a segment to score – even 0 – and none can miss. Although more than one dart can land in the same segment only one order for each set of three can count. How many different ways are there to score 32?

Answer see page **105**

Each same letter in this grid has the same value. What number should replace the question mark and what is the value of each letter?

Answer see page **105**

A	B	B	A	**30**
C	C	A	B	**?**
A	A	B	C	
A	C	C	A	

26   **33**

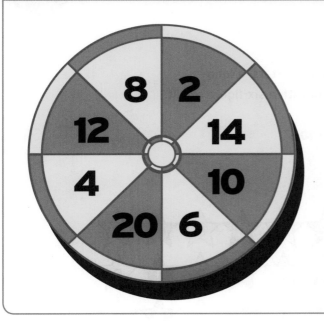

You have three darts to throw at this strange dartboard. Each dart must score and more than one dart can land in the same segment, but separate scoring rounds may not contain the same three values in a different order. How many different ways are there to score 32?

Answer see page **105**

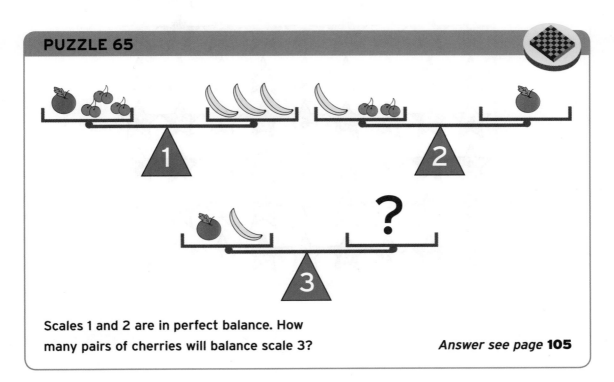

Scales 1 and 2 are in perfect balance. How many pairs of cherries will balance scale 3?

Answer see page **105**

Find hidden within the stars, a long
multiplication sum with a six-figure result.

Answer see page **105**

A

midnight

B

p.m.

This clock was correct at midnight (A), but began to lose 3.75 minutes per hour from that moment. It stopped half an hour ago (B), having run for less than 24 hours. What is the correct time now?

Answer see page **105**

PUZZLE 68

Scales 1 and 2 are in perfect balance. How many stars are required to balance scale 3?

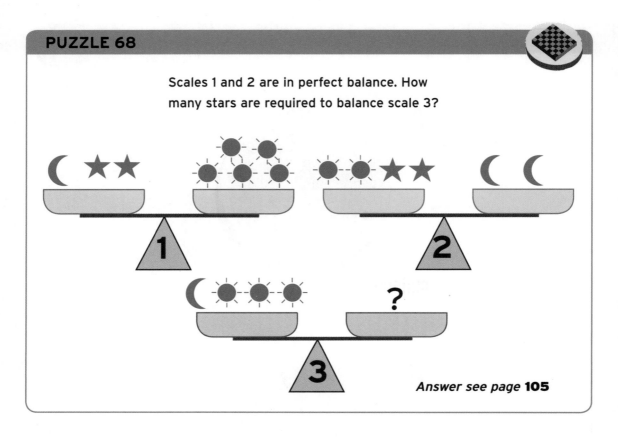

Answer see page **105**

PUZZLE 69

Which of these discs is the odd one out?

Answer see page **105**

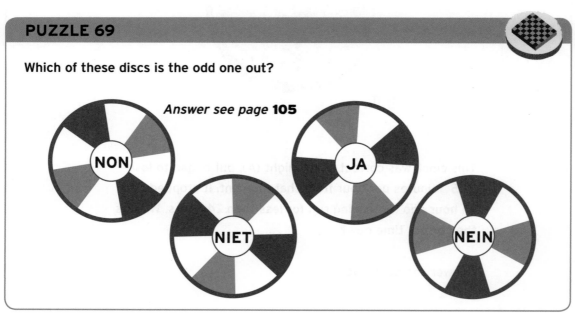

PUZZLE 70

Each shape has a value. Scales 1 and 2 are
in perfect balance. How many squares are
needed to balance scale 3?

Answer see page **105**

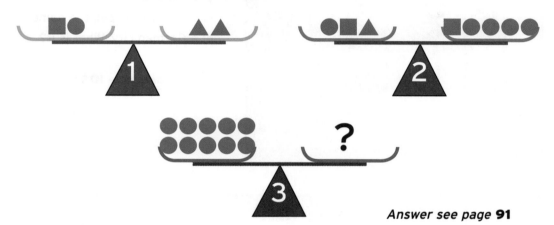

Answer see page **91**

PUZZLE 71

The hands on these clocks move in a strange but
logical way. What is the time on the fourth clock?

Answer see page **105**

C D E F
I J K L
N O P Q
S T V W
X Y Z

Here is the alphabet with some letters omitted. When you found all the missing ones, they will spell the name of a German city. What is it?

Answer see page **106**

PUZZLE 73

What numbers should surround the fourth triangle?

Answer see page **106**

20
6   2

15
12   4

10
18   8

?

PUZZLE 74

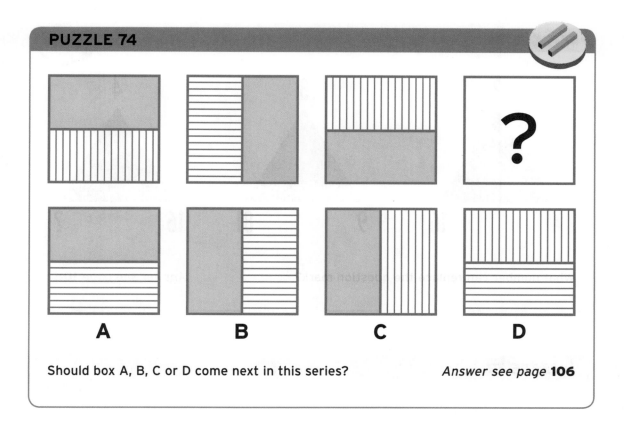

A **B** **C** **D**

Should box A, B, C or D come next in this series?

Answer see page **106**

PUZZLE 75

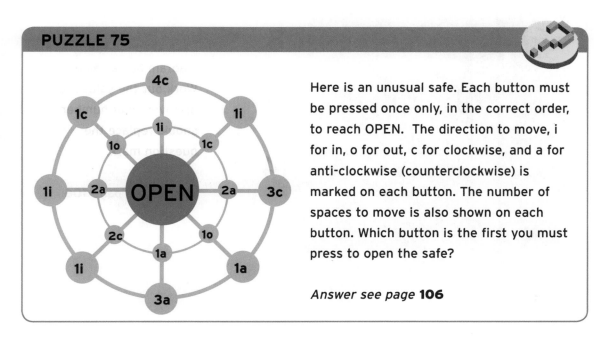

Here is an unusual safe. Each button must be pressed once only, in the correct order, to reach OPEN. The direction to move, i for in, o for out, c for clockwise, and a for anti-clockwise (counterclockwise) is marked on each button. The number of spaces to move is also shown on each button. Which button is the first you must press to open the safe?

Answer see page **106**

PUZZLE 76

2

8

4   16

3

27

9   81

4

?

16   ?

What number can replace the question mark?

Answer see page **106**

PUZZLE 77

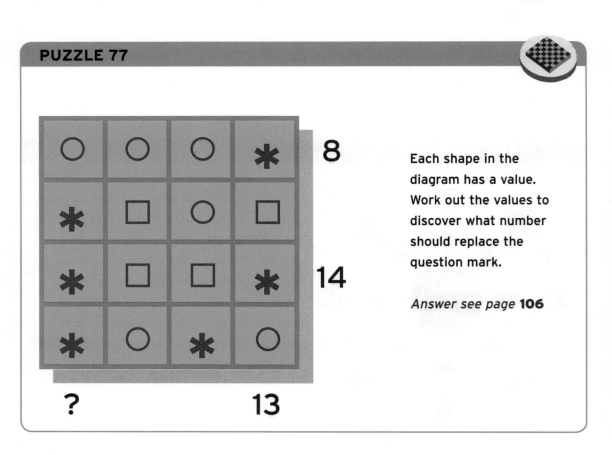

8

14

?   13

Each shape in the diagram has a value. Work out the values to discover what number should replace the question mark.

Answer see page **106**

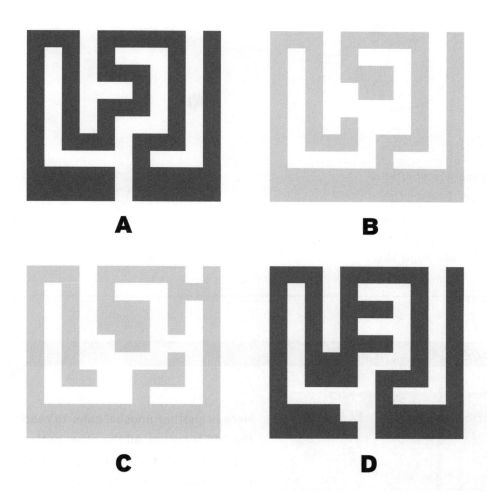

Use logic to find which shape has
the greatest perimeter.

Answer see page **106**

PUZZLE 79

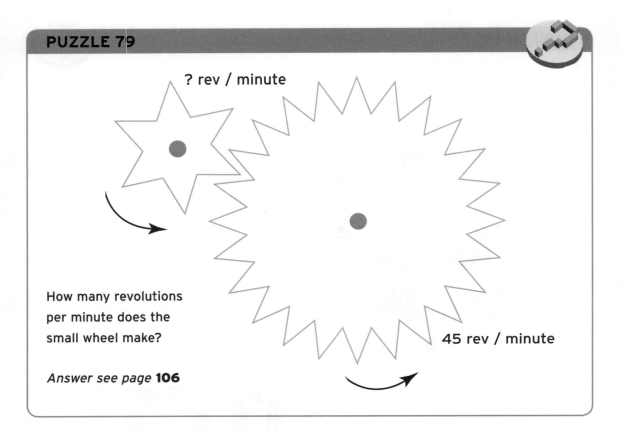

? rev / minute

How many revolutions per minute does the small wheel make?

Answer see page **106**

45 rev / minute

PUZZLE 80

4SE	1E	4S	1SE	4SW
2S	1E	1NE	1SE	1SW
1E	1NW	OPEN	2NW	2W
3E	3NE	1SW	3NW	1SW
2N	1N	1N	3N	1N

Here is another unusual safe. To reach the OPEN button, all the other buttons must be pressed in the correct order. Each button has a compass direction together with the number of steps needed. Which is the first button you must press?

Answer see page **106**

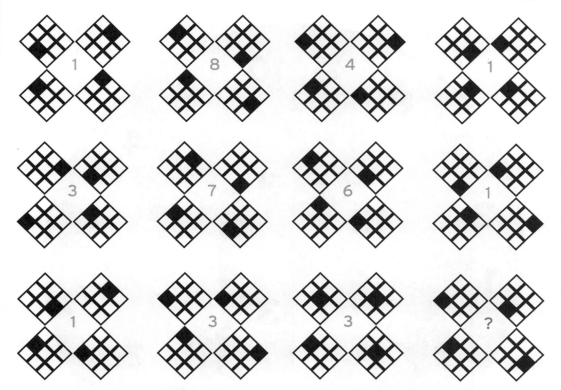

The values represented by the black
segments surrounding each number are
processed in two stages to get the numbers
in the middle of each system. Find the
missing number.

Answer see page **106**

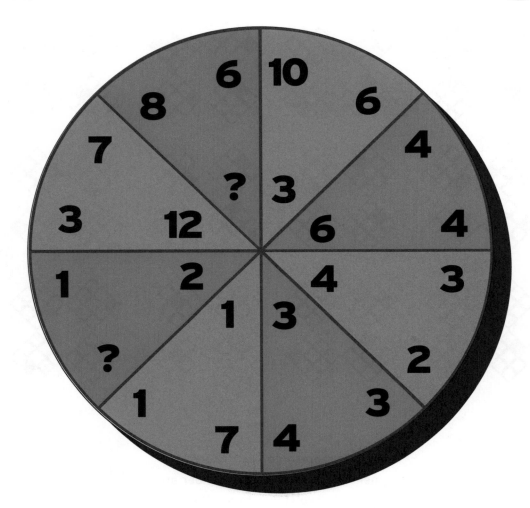

Which two numbers should replace the question marks?

Answer see page **106**

Insert the rows into the appropriate places in the grid to make all lines, columns, and long diagonals add to 105.

27	25	16

-2	-4	36

14	5	3

18	9	0

2	-7	33

			39			
			31			
			23			
35	26	24	15	6	4	-5
			7			
			-1			
			-9			

-6	34	32

19	17	8

38	29	20

-3	37	28

10	1	-8

22	13	11

30	21	12

Answer see page **106**

Edinburgh	50
Cardiff	30
Bristol	20
Aberdeen	?
Ipswich	90

On this strange signpost how far should it be to Aberdeen?

Answer see page **106**

Remove eight of these straight lines to leave only two squares. How can this be done?

Answer see page **107**

PUZZLE 86

J B M R O A
J H   A
H   O
A   U
N   E
T A E T N B

The names of one former baseball star and one former American football star have been hidden in this frame. Who are they?

Answer see page **107**

PUZZLE 87

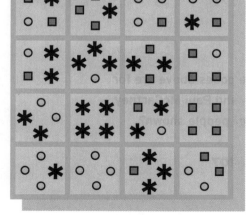

Which two boxes in the diagram are similar?

Answer see page **107**

Michael Jackson =

Paul McCartney =

1

2

3

4

5

If the semaphore codes above are for
Michael Jackson and Paul McCartney,
who are the other people shown?

Answer see page **107**

PUZZLE 89

Start at the far left circle and move - to the right only - along the lines to the far right circle, collecting the numbers and the ovals as you go. An oval is worth -37. How many routes give 152?

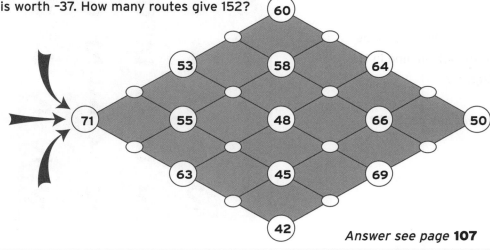

Answer see page **107**

PUZZLE 90

2	1	4	7
5	4	5	9
3	1	8	6
8	3	?	4

What number should replace the question mark?

Answer see page **107**

PUZZLE 91

What number should be on the bottom line in this diagram?

Answer see page **107**

8	6	5	3	6
5	1	5	2	4
3	5	0	1	2
1	6	5	1	2
?	?	?	?	?

PUZZLE 92

Each shape has a value. Scales 1 and 2 are in perfect balance.
How many squares are needed to balance scale 3?

Answer see page **107**

PUZZLE 93

What number should replace the question mark?

Answer see page **107**

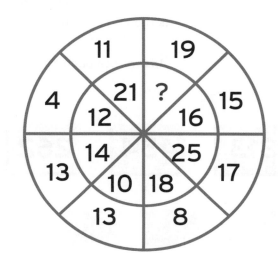

PUZZLE 94

This grid of compass directions follows a set pattern in a continuous horizontal line. What direction is missing and what is the order?

Answer see page **107**

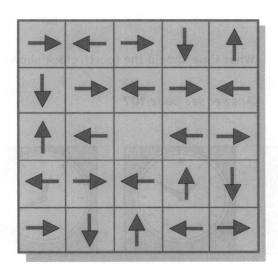

N

Which of the following numbers
is the odd one out?

Answer see page **107**

A

| 313 | 454 | 262 | 695 | 727 |

B

| 4 | 8 | 10 | 32 | 64 | 128 |

What time should the fourth clock show?

Answer see page **107**

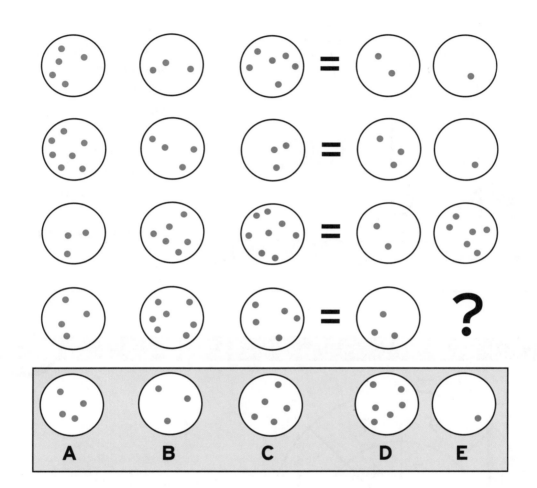

Which Petri dish of bacteria cultures should replace the question mark?

Answer see page **107**

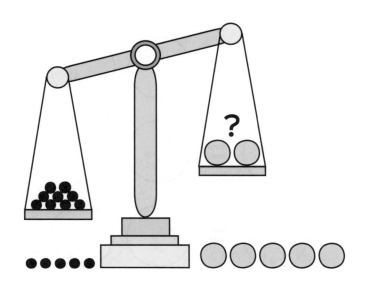

If each large ball weighs one and a third times the weight of each little ball, what is the minimum number of balls that need to be added to the right-hand side to make the scales balance?

Answer see page **107**

What number should replace the question mark?

Answer see page **107**

G	X	R	V	F	S	H	P	L	A
D	A	N	U	B	E	Q	F	Z	K
R	P	N	E	N	I	H	R	W	Q
C	Y	F	A	J	N	M	F	J	D
Z	K	E	B	I	E	B	L	E	H
E	B	M	B	U	D	G	E	T	H
R	D	U	S	R	Y	N	Q	V	F
I	Z	E	Q	W	O	J	A	P	X
O	N	P	J	H	T	A	G	U	S
L	Y	G	R	X	V	N	N	B	G

The ten longest rivers in Europe are hidden in this grid. Each is spelled in a straight line, up, down, across or diagonally, forward or backward with no letters missed nor any gaps. Can you find them? They are:

Danube   Meuse
Ebro   Rhine
Elbe   Rhone
Guandiana   Seine
Loire   Tagus

Answer see page 107

1   2   3   4

What time should the fourth clock show?

Answer see page **108**

What number should replace
the question mark?

Answer see page **108**

6	7	4	8
2	3	0	0
4	5	2	4
5	6	3	?

A **B**

C **D**

Should A, B, C, or D come next in this series?

Answer see page **108**

A

midnight

B

a.m.

This clock was correct at midnight (A), but lost one minute per hour from that moment on. It stopped one hour ago (B), having run for less than 24 hours. What is the time now?

Answer see page **108**

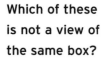

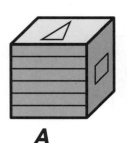

A

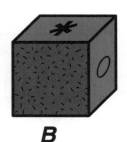

B

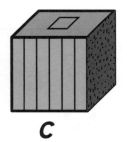

C

D

E

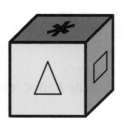

F

Which of these is not a view of the same box?

Answer see page **108**

PUZZLE 106

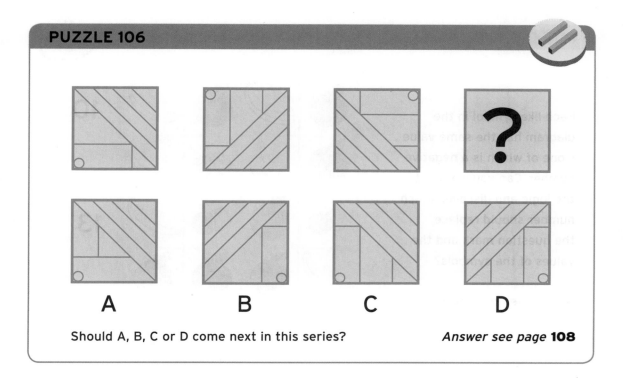

A B C D

Should A, B, C or D come next in this series?

Answer see page **108**

PUZZLE 107

What number should replace the question mark?

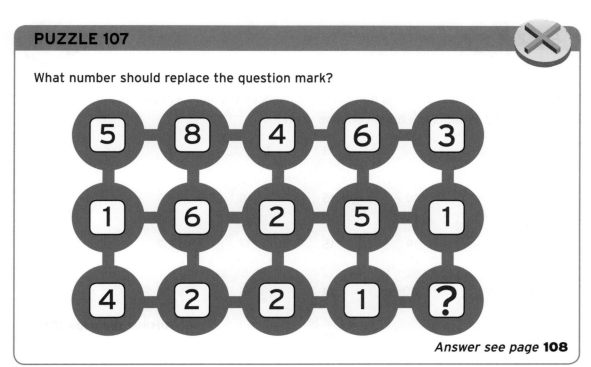

Answer see page **108**

Each like symbol in the diagram has the same value – one of which is a negative number. Can you work out the logic and discover which number should replace the question mark and the values of the symbols?

Answer see page 108

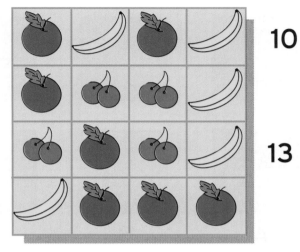

10

13

15   ?

Start at the far left circle and move – to the right only – along the lines to the far right circle, collecting numbers and ovals as you go. Each oval has a value of -20. What is the most common score?

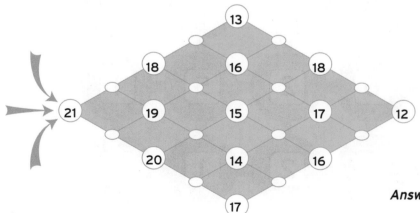

Answer see page 108

PUZZLE 110

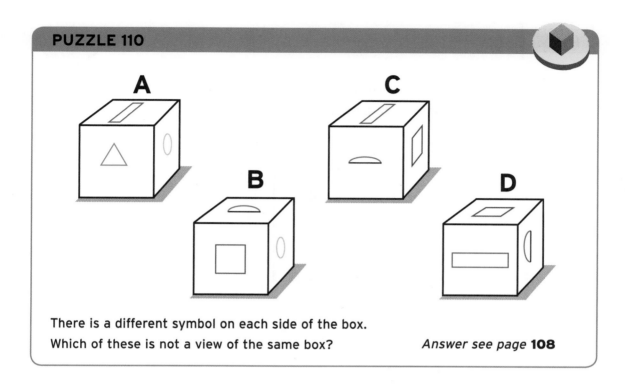

There is a different symbol on each side of the box.

Which of these is not a view of the same box?

Answer see page **108**

PUZZLE 111

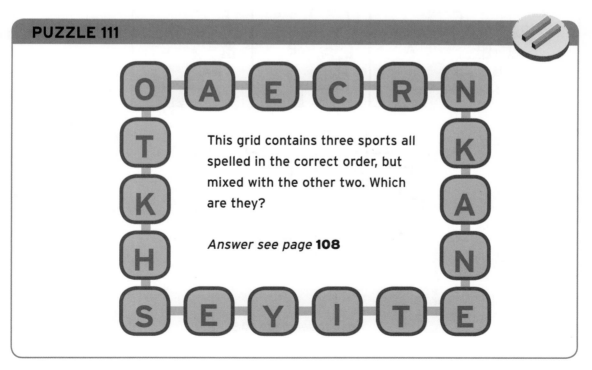

This grid contains three sports all spelled in the correct order, but mixed with the other two. Which are they?

Answer see page **108**

Which piece can be put with the one
above it to form a perfect square?

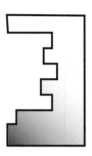

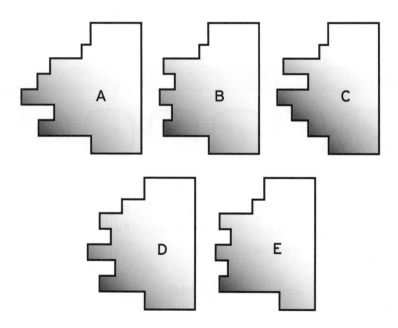

Answer see page **108**

Use logic to discover which shape has the greatest perimeter.

Answer see page **108**

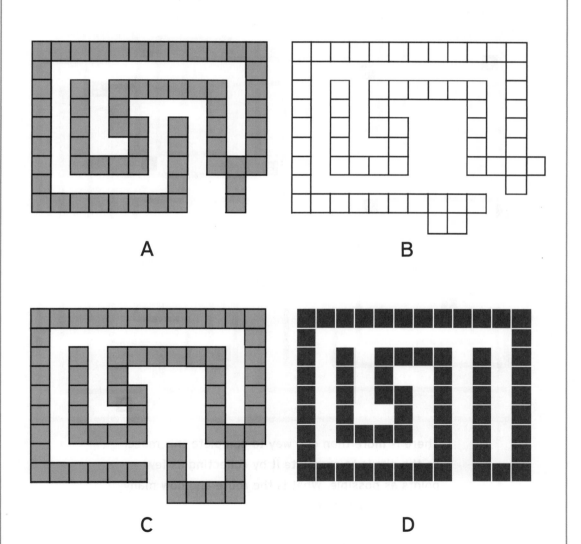

A

B

C

D

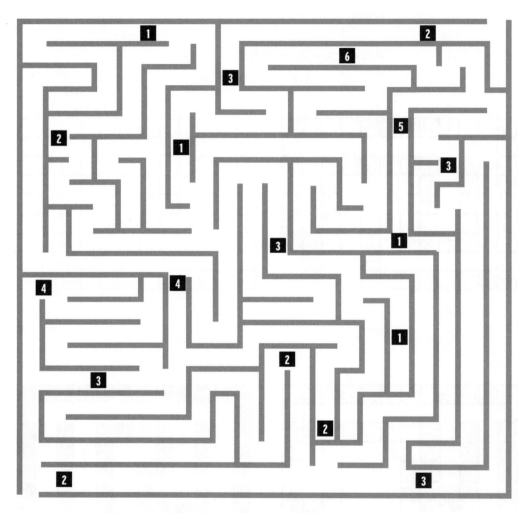

There is more than one way to complete this maze, so the aim is to complete it by collecting as few points as possible. What is the route and how many points are collected?

Answer see page **108**

PUZZLE 115

What number should replace
the question mark?

Answer see page **108**

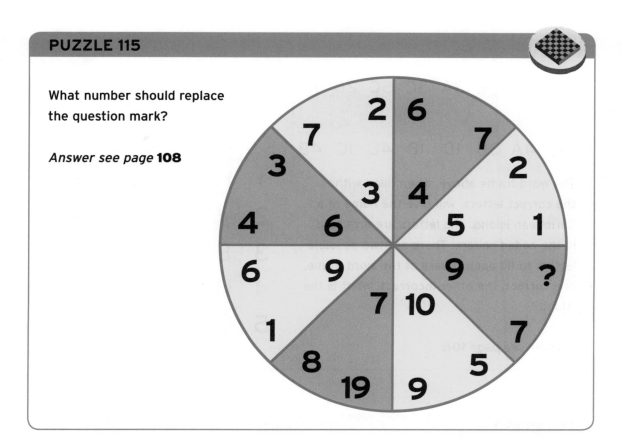

PUZZLE 116

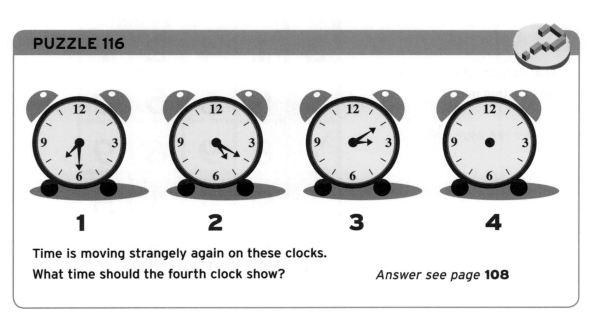

1   **2**   **3**   **4**

Time is moving strangely again on these clocks.
What time should the fourth clock show?

Answer see page **108**

2B 1B 2E 3A 3C 5C 2D 1A

3E 4A 3D 1D 1B 4E 1C 4B

The word frame above, when filled with
the correct letters, will give the name of a
Caribbean island. The letters are arranged
in the coded square. There are two possible
letters to fill each square of the word frame,
one correct, the other incorrect. What is the
island?

Answer see page **108**

	A	B	C	D	E
1	H	A	O	B	F
2	V	B	W	T	R
3	E	U	K	M	J
4	U	S	P	A	I
5	G	Z	D	G	X

What number should replace
the question mark?

Answer see page **108**

3	1	4	2	7
5	6	6	5	0
7	8	9	6	9
1	9	4	1	5
2	6	?	2	5

Four of these animals have something
in common. Which is the odd one out?
(Clue: think diets)

Answer see page **108**

Which route should the bear
take to get to the woods?

Answer see page **109**

PUZZLE 121

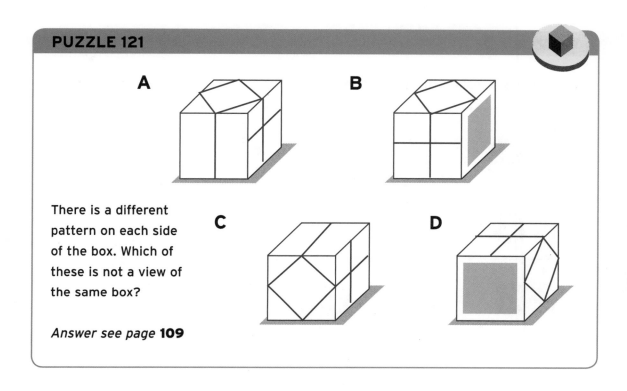

A

B

C

D

There is a different pattern on each side of the box. Which of these is not a view of the same box?

Answer see page **109**

PUZZLE 122

Start at the far left circle and move – to the right only – along the lines to the far right circle, collecting the numbers and the ovals as you go. Each oval has a value of minus 13. What are the minimum and maximum totals possible?

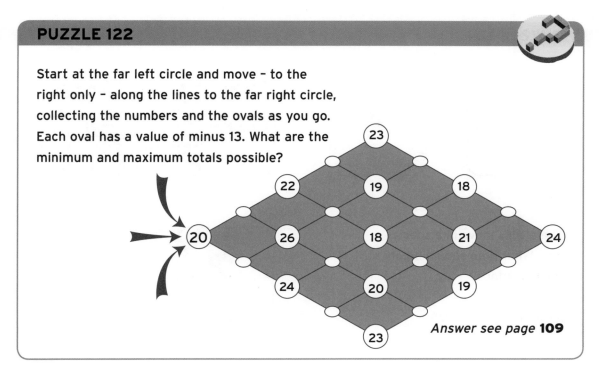

Answer see page **109**

PUZZLE 123

What numbers replace the question marks?

Answer see page **109**

4	7	4	9	5
8	5	1	3	6
3	7	6	?	?

PUZZLE 124

The clocks move in a special way. What time should be on the blank face?

Answer see page **109**

PUZZLE 125

What number should replace
the question mark?

Answer see page **109**

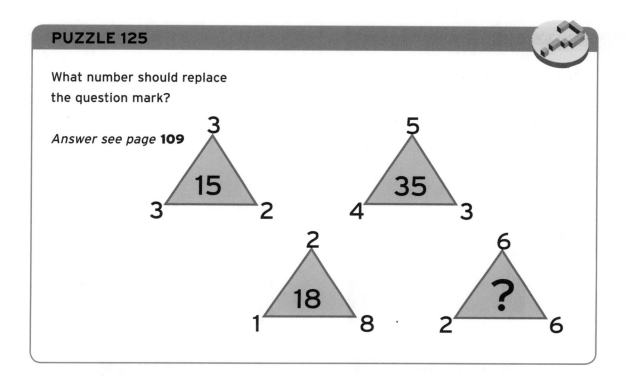

PUZZLE 126

Start at the far left circle and move, to the
right only, along the lines to the far right
circle, collecting numbers and ovals as you
go. Each oval has a value of −41. How many
routes give 0?

Answer see page **109**

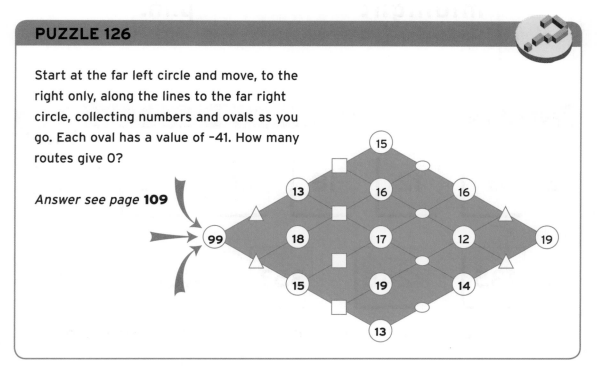

PUZZLE 127

This clock was correct at midnight (A), but began to lose 10 minutes per hour from that moment. It stopped 2 ½ hours ago (B), having run for less than 24 hours. What is the correct time now?

Answer see page **109**

A

midnight

B

p.m.

PUZZLE 128

A	6	12	18	26	30	36

B	135	246	357	468	689

Which of the numbers in each line is the odd one out?   *Answer see page* **109**

PUZZLE 129

Above is the code for SUMMER HOLIDAYS. What is written on each line below?

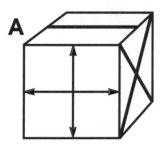

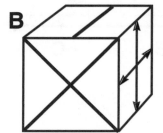

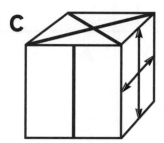

Answer see page **109**

PUZZLE 130

Which of these is not a view of the same three sides of a box?

Answer see page **109**

A   B   C

Which two boxes in this
diagram are similar?

Answer see page **109**

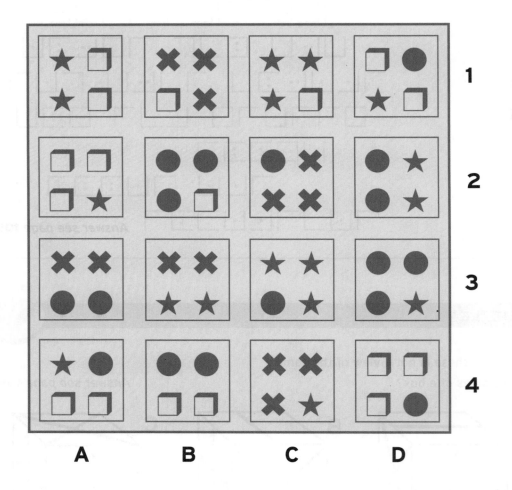

PUZZLE 132

The arrows in this grid go in a clockwise spiral starting from the top left corner. In which direction should the missing arrow point?

Answer see page **109**

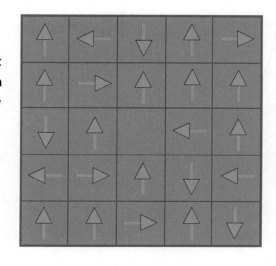

N

PUZZLE 133

What time should the fourth clock show?

Answer see page **109**

Easy Answers

EASY ANSWERS

ANSWER 1
Left to right: 24, 22, 25, 23.
★ = 7, ● = 6, ■ = 5.

ANSWER 2
C.

ANSWER 3
13. ★ = 3, ● = 2, ■ = 5.

ANSWER 4
3D in column 1 on row 2.

ANSWER 5

2	4	7	3	1
4	6	0	5	1
7	0	1	2	4
3	5	2	6	8
1	1	4	8	9

ANSWER 6
A. 33. Each number rises by 9.
B. 16. The squares of 1, 2, 3, 4 and 5.

ANSWER 7
A.

ANSWER 8
C.

ANSWER 9
7. It is a run of consecutive prime numbers.

ANSWER 10
2 squares.

ANSWER 11
A4 and D1.

ANSWER 12
Nein. The others are "yes" in European languages. Nein is "no" in German.

ANSWER 13
B1 and A3.

ANSWER 14
8. Heart = -2, Diamond = 3, Club = 4.

ANSWER 15
A. 8 rows of three rabbits
B. 28 rows of two rabbits
C. 6 rabbits in three rows of three rabbits can be done like this:

ANSWER 16
1. Monet
2. Dali
3. Rembrandt
4. Donatello
5. Ernst
6. van Gogh

ANSWER 17
3. In each row, subtract the middle number from the left to give the right.

ANSWER 18
5.25.

ANSWER 19

Switzerland

ANSWER 20

ANSWER 21

Mike Tyson.

ANSWER 22

1	5	4	7	6
5	2	0	3	3
4	0	8	5	8
7	3	5	2	6
6	3	8	6	4

ANSWER 23

Lowest is 45, highest is 83.

ANSWER 24

Beethoven.

ANSWER 25

A. Galileo
B. Archimedes
C. Oppenheimer
D. Einstein
E. Heisenberg
F. Bell
G. Fleming
H. Ampere
I. Celsius
J. Pascal

ANSWER 26

East.

ANSWER 27

2U on row 4 in column 4.

ANSWER 28

6	8	1	2	4
8	0	9	5	2
1	9	9	6	7
2	5	6	5	1
4	2	7	1	3

ANSWER 29

31. It is the only odd number.

ANSWER 30

9	1	4	6	3
1	2	5	3	1
4	5	8	0	2
6	3	0	9	6
3	1	2	6	7

ANSWER 31

4 each of $1, 25c, 5c and 1c.

ANSWER 32

10. The numbers in each sector are added together and the diagonally opposite sectors have the same total.

ANSWER 33

8.05. The clocks move 4 hours and 50 minutes forward each time.

ANSWER 34

Orange. The numbers are added, an even total produces an orange triangle, an odd one produces pink.

ANSWER 35

44. Add the three outer numbers together, double them and put the answer in the middle.

ANSWER 36
8.

ANSWER 37
F.

ANSWER 38
3 diamonds.

ANSWER 39
5 minutes past 5.

ANSWER 40
2.45. The hour hand moves forward 2 hours each time, the minute hand moves alternately forward 5 minutes and back 10.

ANSWER 41
14. Diamond = 6, Heart = 4, Club = 3.

ANSWER 42
5a in the inner circle.

ANSWER 43
9.15. In each case the hour hand moves forward 1 hour and the minute hand 15 minutes forward.

ANSWER 44
Minimum is 97, maximum is 105.

ANSWER 45

4	5	1	9	2
5	6	3	1	4
1	3	9	5	1
9	1	5	7	8
2	4	1	8	2

ANSWER 46
West. The order is West, South, East, North, North, and it runs continuously down column 1, up column 2, down column 3, etc.

ANSWER 47
E.

ANSWER 48
4.

ANSWER 49
21. ★ = 5, ● = 4, ■ = 8.

ANSWER 50
52. ★ = 17, ● = 13, ■ = 21.

ANSWER 51
D. The small square moves clockwise with the circle gaining an extra line each time. The T moves anti(counter)-clockwise and rotates through 180°.

ANSWER 52
1. Subtract the top row from the middle row to give the bottom row.

ANSWER 53
8. Add the first row to the second row to give the third row.

ANSWER 54
C. The circle moves 90° anti (counter)

clockwise, the straight line moves 45°
clockwise and the rectangle moves 90°
clockwise.

ANSWER 55

The numbers at the top, middle and
left are consecutive. The top and left
numbers are then added together to give
the right number.

8   12

ANSWER 56

18. ★ = 6, ● = 5, ■ = 4.

ANSWER 57

6. Subtract the two bottom numbers
from the top number to give the middle
number.

ANSWER 58

0 and 5. Subtract the lower line from
the one immediately above it and put the
answer directly below.

ANSWER 59

1 and 6. On each row, add the two outer
numbers to give the middle one.

ANSWER 60

In A, 65. All the others are divisible by 10.
In B, 400. All the others are divisible by 9.

ANSWER 61

E.

ANSWER 62

8 ways.

ANSWER 63

29. A = 11, B = 4, C = 7.

ANSWER 64

8 ways.

ANSWER 65

7 pairs of cherries.

ANSWER 66

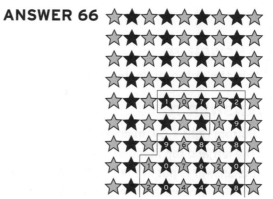

ANSWER 67

8.30 pm.

ANSWER 68

4 stars.

ANSWER 69

Ja. The others are "no" in European
languages. Nein is "yes" in German.

ANSWER 70

2 squares.

ANSWER 71

6.55

ANSWER 72

Hamburg.

ANSWER 73

The right number doubles;
the left number goes up by
6 and the top number goes down by 5.

ANSWER 74

B.

ANSWER 75

1i in the outer circle, between 1i and 1c.

ANSWER 76

Bottom right = 64, middle = 256.
The left and top numbers are multiplied and the answer is put in the middle. The top and middle numbers are then multiplied and this answer goes to the right.

ANSWER 77

16. ★ = 5, ● = 1, ■ = 2.

ANSWER 78

A. The thinnest shape to cover an area always has the greatest perimeter.

ANSWER 79

180 revolutions. (45 revolutions x 24 teeth of big wheel [1080 movements]) ÷ 6 (teeth of small wheel) = 180.

ANSWER 80

1E on row 2, column 2.

ANSWER 81

5. Use the values represented by the black spots in the puzzle, numbered as below. Multiply each top pair of values together to get the values for the bottom pair, and subtract the bottom left value from the top right value.
4 x 7 = 28; 7 - 2 = 5.

ANSWER 82

Outer 3, inner 9. The numbers in the outer sectors are added together and the sums of the top half are double those of the diagonally opposite bottom halves. The top half numbers in the inner part of the sectors are three times those of the diagonally opposite bottom half ones.

ANSWER 83

10	1	-8	39	30	21	12
2	-7	33	31	22	13	11
-6	34	32	23	14	5	3
35	26	24	15	6	4	-5
27	25	16	7	-2	-4	36
19	17	8	-1	-3	37	28
18	9	0	-9	38	29	20

ANSWER 84

10. This is the alphanumeric value of the town's first letter, multiplied by 10.

ANSWER 85

ANSWER 86

Babe Ruth and Joe Montana.

ANSWER 87

2A and 3C.

ANSWER 88

1. Phil Collins.
2. Michael Schumacher.
3. Sean Connery.
4. Mike Tyson.
5. John Lennon.

ANSWER 89

4 ways.

ANSWER 90

2. The outer numbers, when multiplied, give the inner one.

ANSWER 91

18500. Each line is deducted from the the line above to give the line below.

ANSWER 92

24 squares.

ANSWER 93

16. The sum of inner and diagonally opposite outer segments totals 29.

ANSWER 94

East. The order is E, W, E, S, N, W.

ANSWER 95

A. 695. The other numbers have the same first and third digits.
B. 10. The numbers double each time and this should be 16.

ANSWER 96

12.30. Each clock moves forward 1 hour and 10 minutes.

ANSWER 97

B. Count the bacteria in each Petri dish, then multiply the first number by the second number and add the third number to the product. The 2-digit result follows. (4 x 7) + 5 = 33.

ANSWER 98

5 (4 big and 1 little).

ANSWER 99

4. The sum of diagonally opposite segments are the same. 6 + 4 = 8 + 2.

ANSWER 100

G	X	R	V	F	S	H	P	L	A
D	A	N	U	B	E	Q	F	Z	K
R	P	N	E	N	I	H	R	W	Q
C	Y	F	A	J	N	M	F	J	D
Z	K	E	B	I	E	B	L	E	H
E	B	M	B	U	D	G	E	T	H
R	D	U	S	R	Y	N	Q	V	F
I	Z	E	Q	W	Q	J	A	P	X
O	N	P	J	H	T	A	G	U	S
L	Y	G	R	X	V	N	N	B	G

ANSWER 101

10.50. The time moves backwards 1 hour, 5 minutes on each clock.

ANSWER 102

Add 1 to the number in the first column to give the second number. Column three has 3 subtracted from column two and column four is double the value of column three.

ANSWER 103

C.

ANSWER 104

6.00 am.

ANSWER 105

E.

ANSWER 106

D.

ANSWER 107

2. Subtract the second row from the top row to give the bottom row.

ANSWER 108

3. Apples = 6, Bananas = -1, Cherries = 4.

ANSWER 109

4 (26 ways).

ANSWER 110

B.

ANSWER 111

Hockey, Karate and Tennis.

ANSWER 112

B.

ANSWER 113

D. The least number of faces touching each other gives the greatest perimeter.

ANSWER 114

The lowest possible scoring route is 9.

ANSWER 115

10. The three numbers in each sector are added together and the totals in the bottom four segments are double those of their diagonally opposite ones.

ANSWER 116

1.00. In each case, the time is moving back 2 hours 10 minutes.

ANSWER 117

Barbados.

ANSWER 118

1. On each row, subtract the two right numbers from the two left ones. The answer is put in the middle.

ANSWER 119

Elephant. All the others are meat-eating animals.

ANSWER 120

ANSWER 121

C.

ANSWER 122

Maximum is 59, minimum is 50.

ANSWER 123

4 and 1. Add the top line to the bottom line to give the middle line.

ANSWER 124

4.20. The times move forward by 1 hour and 5 minutes, 2 hours and 10 minutes, 4 hours and 20 minutes and 8 hours and 40 minutes.

ANSWER 125

48. Add together the bottom two numbers, multiply the total by the top and place the answer in the middle.

ANSWER 126

10

ANSWER 127

1.00am.

ANSWER 128

A. 26. Multiples of 6 should make it 24.
B. 689. The other numbers' digits increase by one.

ANSWER 129

1. Should I sail
2. Did Ray smile
3. Sheila said yes
4. Museum has old dolls
5. She sells sea shells

ANSWER 130

B.

ANSWER 131

A4 and D1.

ANSWER 132

N. The sequence is NWSNEN.

ANSWER 133

7.10. The clock moves 15, 20 and 25 minutes forward.

Medium Puzzles

This is where things start to warm up. By this point, you should have developed a reasonable feel for the types of puzzle in this book, and the basic ways in which they work. You also ought to be getting some idea about the devious minds of the puzzle authors, which will prove invaluable in the pages to come. In the pages that follow, we'll challenge you to push your brain up a gear and really start getting to grips with the puzzles.

These problems are going to test your logic, deduction, arithmetic and ingenuity. The answers in this section are not obvious. They're designed to make you think seriously about the possible answers. You may need to forget about being able to spot solutions, and fall back on the first principles for each puzzle – how to analyse each problem, break it down to its essential components, squeeze all the information you need out of it, and put it back together again in such a way as to let you glean the answer.

Don't be disheartened if you find this section slower going than the one before. Everyone will need to take this section more seriously than the one before. Even the most hardened puzzle supremos will find themselves breaking stride to examine these problems carefully. This is where you'll find the meat of your mental workout – a few sets of these problems will leave your mind well and truly pumped.

The names of the following ten car manufacturers can be found in this grid on vertical, horizontal and diagonal lines.
Can you find them?

Answer see page **136**

Citroen

Jaguar

Peugeot

Renault

Rolls Royce

Rover

Skoda

Toyota

Volkswagen

Yugo

R	N	B	L	F	K	X	C	D	R
E	N	D	C	W	Q	H	S	O	E
N	E	G	A	W	S	K	L	O	V
A	O	H	J	K	O	L	B	P	O
U	R	G	V	D	S	F	Y	J	R
L	T	C	A	R	A	U	G	A	J
T	I	T	O	E	G	U	E	P	M
P	C	Y	T	O	Y	O	T	A	B
J	C	F	V	G	Z	C	W	D	K
E	K	D	P	M	H	Q	G	Y	F

PUZZLE 135

If the name Elizabeth Taylor is

⌐•⌐>⌐⌐∟∨• ∨⌐>•⊓⌐

Who are the other legendary film stars?

1. ><•
   •⌐>•⌐∟⌐•

2. ⌐⌐⌐> ⌐• ⌐•⌐∨

3. ⌐•⌐⌐•
   ⌐⌐•⌐•∟

*Answer see page **136***

PUZZLE 136

O	T	E	S	I	O	T	I
M	O	P	S	L	B	G	R
E	O	G	N	D	N	G	O
N	E	B	O	R	A	I	O
H	V	E	J	D	L	M	T
S	R	A	E	F	D	R	N
E	W	B	U	A	I	R	C
O	I	M	N	E	R	E	T

A knight, which moves either one square horizontally and two vertically or two horizontally and one vertically, starts at the shaded square of this chess board visiting each square without returning to the same square twice. Find the route which spells out six famous movie stars.

*Answer see page **136***

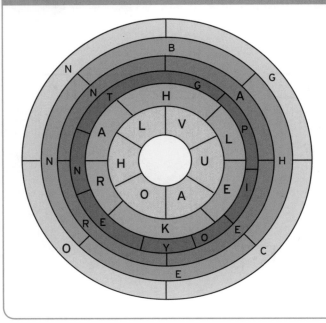

Turn the dial on this diagram to give 11 names of lakes from around the world. (7 or over is a good score.)

Answer see page **136**

A knight, which moves either one square horizontally and two vertically or two horizontally and one vertically, is positioned on this chess board on position B2. If you move to all the squares in the right sequence, without visiting any square twice, you will find the names of five famous golfers.

Answer see page **136**

O	P	C	A	O	R	N
K	A	T	Y	I	P	D
L	M	L	R	C	N	A
R	P	I	Y	M	L	D
W	A	E	K	N	G	O
R	N	E	T	C	L	A
R	A	I	O	F	S	E

PUZZLE 139

If the term ancient gods is

Who are these gods?

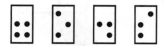

1.

2.

3.

4.

5.

Answer see page **136**

PUZZLE 140

Can you work out what letter needs to be inserted in the middle to form four airlines by combining opposite segments?

Answer see page **136**

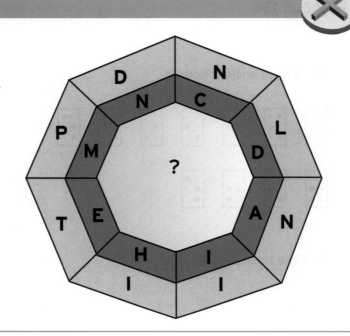

PUZZLE 141

If the word scientist is

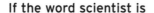

who are these scientists?

1.
2.
3.
4.
5.
6.

Answer see page **136**

PUZZLE 142

The names of the following ten perfumes can be found in this grid on vertical, horizontal and diagonal lines. Can you find them?

Answer see page **136**

Amarige

Anais-Anais

Coco

Dune

Miss Dior

Obsession

Paris

Safari

Samsara

Spellbound

S	I	A	N	A	S	I	A	N	A
A	P	D	G	H	F	P	J	C	R
F	C	E	G	I	R	A	M	A	A
A	F	H	L	D	J	R	K	F	S
R	Y	Q	U	L	Z	I	Z	R	M
I	R	N	Z	X	B	S	F	X	A
Q	E	V	K	W	O	O	Y	J	S
B	H	K	V	D	W	C	U	G	I
O	B	S	E	S	S	I	O	N	G
R	O	I	D	S	S	I	M	C	D

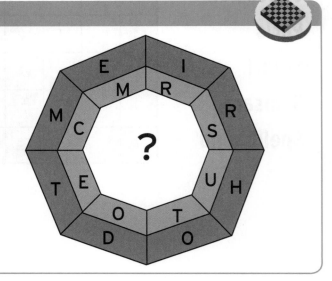

Turn the dials on this diagram to give 8 forenames and 8 surnames of famous actresses. Then match them up to give their full names. Who are they? (A score above 5 is very good!)

Answer see page **136**

Can you work out what letter needs to be inserted in the middle to form four artists by combining opposite segments?

Answer see page **137**

The names of the following ten film stars can be found in this grid on vertical, horizontal and diagonal lines. Can you find them?

Answer see page **137**

W	Z	Q	E	P	R	V	H	E	F	M
T	O	U	S	Y	J	A	H	E	E	Z
T	N	S	I	G	K	L	U	L	S	W
I	I	E	U	F	H	K	G	E	E	P
P	C	A	R	H	X	I	H	C	E	H
D	A	N	C	H	B	L	G	U	L	J
A	P	P	M	S	Q	M	R	R	C	R
R	L	E	O	J	R	E	A	B	N	G
B	A	N	T	T	Z	R	N	P	H	Y
S	K	N	A	H	M	O	T	W	O	S
Y	R	B	X	F	Q	J	X	N	J	S

John Cleese	Val Kilmer
Tom Cruise	Bruce Lee
Mel Gibson	Al Pacino
Hugh Grant	Sean Penn
Tom Hanks	Brad Pitt

Turn the dials on this unusual safe to give 12 surnames of sports stars from the past and present. (More than 8 is a good score.)

Answer see page **137**

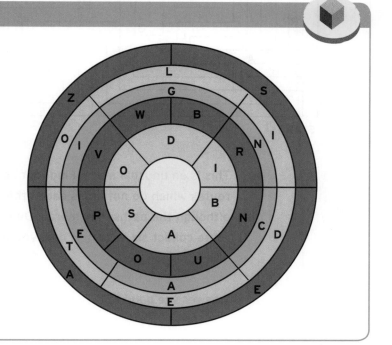

FINISH

START

This is an unusual maze. Find four separate routes which do not cross each other, although the paths may merge. On each route collect six letters to give you four US cities.

Answer see page **137**

If the names Diego Maradona and Jack Charlton are

⊔◖O⊏⊐⊓ ⊓⊔◖⌐⊔⊔⊓◖⌐⊔

and

◖⊔⊔⊏ ⊔◖⊐⊔⌐◖∨⊓◖

Who are the other footballers?

1. ⌐⊓◖⊔⌐∨⊓ ◖⊔⊐⊐O⊓

2. ◖⊔⌐⊓⊓O∨ ◖⊔⌐⊐⊏⊔⊓⊓

3. ⊏⌐<◖O⊓ ⊏⌐⌐⊐⊔⊓

4. ⌐⌐O⊔ ⊔⊔⊓∨⊓◖⊔

5. ◖<⌐⊐⌐⊓ ⊏⌐O⊓∨⊓⊔⊓◖⊓

*Answer see page **137***

PUZZLE 149

Rearrange these boxes in a 3 x 3 square in such a way that the adjoining letters are always the same. Then add the alphanumeric values of each line of three outer letters and convert back to letters to give the name of a Roman god.

*Answer see page **137***

PUZZLE 150

FINISH

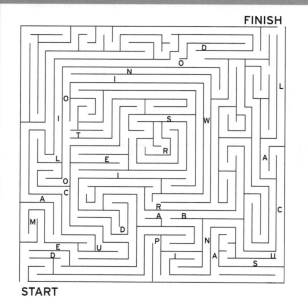

START

This is an unusual maze. Find four separate routes through it without any route crossing another, although the paths may merge. On each route collect six letters to give you four scientists.

Who are they?

*Answer see page **137***

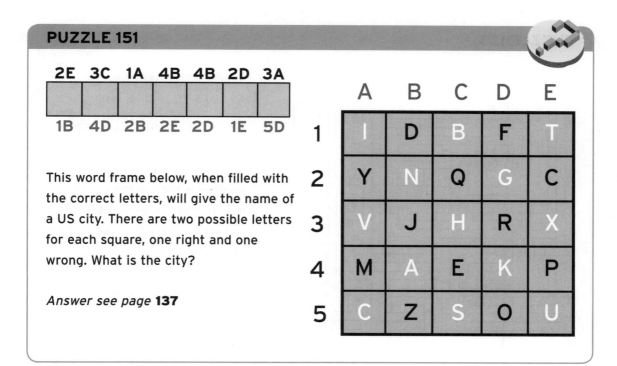

2E 3C 1A 4B 4B 2D 3A

1B 4D 2B 2E 2D 1E 5D

	A	B	C	D	E
1	I	D	B	F	T
2	Y	N	Q	G	C
3	V	J	H	R	X
4	M	A	E	K	P
5	C	Z	S	O	U

This word frame below, when filled with the correct letters, will give the name of a US city. There are two possible letters for each square, one right and one wrong. What is the city?

Answer see page 137

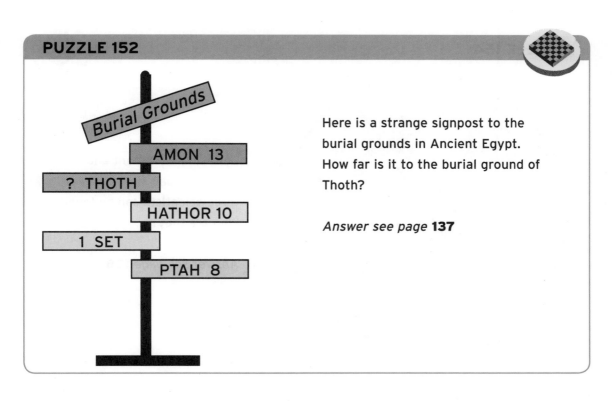

Burial Grounds

AMON 13

? THOTH

HATHOR 10

1 SET

PTAH 8

Here is a strange signpost to the burial grounds in Ancient Egypt. How far is it to the burial ground of Thoth?

Answer see page 137

PUZZLE 153

FINISH

START

This is an unusual maze. Find four separate routes through it without any route crossing another, although the paths may merge. On each route collect 6 letters to give you four musical terms.

Answer see page **138**

PUZZLE 154

By taking a segment and finding its pair the names of three scientists can be found. Who are they?

Answer see page **138**

PUZZLE 155

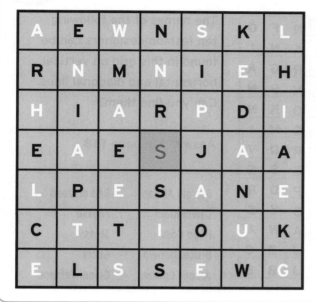

A	E	W	N	S	K	L
R	N	M	N	I	E	H
H	I	A	R	P	D	I
E	A	E	S	J	A	A
L	P	E	S	A	N	E
C	T	T	I	O	U	K
E	L	S	S	E	W	G

A knight, which moves either one square horizontally and two vertically or two horizontally and one vertically, starts at the shaded square of this small chess board visiting each square without returning to the same square twice. Find the route which spells out four famous writers.

Answer see page **138**

PUZZLE 156

The names of the following ten furniture makers can be found in this grid on either vertical, horizontal or diagonal lines.
Can you find them?

Answer see page **138**

Adam	Lock
Chippendale	Phillipponat
Cob	Seddon
Gillow	Sheraton
Hepplewhite	Stuart

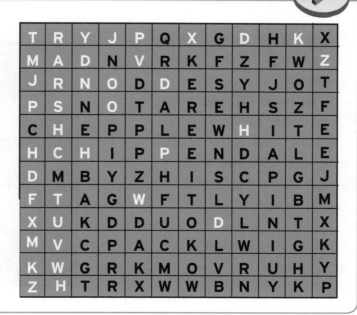

T	R	Y	J	P	Q	X	G	D	H	K	X
M	A	D	N	V	R	K	F	Z	F	W	Z
J	R	N	O	D	D	E	S	Y	J	O	T
P	S	N	O	T	A	R	E	H	S	Z	F
C	H	E	P	P	L	E	W	H	I	T	E
H	C	H	I	P	P	E	N	D	A	L	E
D	M	B	Y	Z	H	I	S	C	P	G	J
F	T	A	G	W	F	T	L	Y	I	B	M
X	U	K	D	D	U	O	D	L	N	T	X
M	V	C	P	A	C	K	L	W	I	G	K
K	W	G	R	K	M	O	V	R	U	H	Y
Z	H	T	R	X	W	W	B	N	Y	K	P

PUZZLE 157

Y	N	J	Z	B	W	K	X	B	T	N	F	G
G	I	O	R	G	I	O	A	R	M	A	N	I
T	E	S	S	O	B	O	G	U	H	R	G	A
X	L	V	E	S	V	R	Y	C	R	N	B	N
R	K	Q	S	H	F	X	B	E	V	O	K	N
Z	N	G	S	W	L	J	D	O	Q	C	M	I
J	I	T	E	M	P	O	F	L	W	R	Q	V
Y	V	K	L	K	R	S	B	D	Z	E	S	E
W	L	N	L	D	B	H	P	F	Q	P	D	R
F	A	T	E	G	U	C	C	I	X	S	Y	S
X	C	A	L	T	P	Q	M	E	H	A	W	A
V	D	G	J	V	Z	D	Y	L	G	J	Z	C
S	T	U	S	S	Y	F	K	D	B	J	B	E

The names of the following ten fashion designers can be found in this grid on vertical, horizontal and diagonal lines. Can you find them?

Answer see page 138

Giorgio Armani	Red or Dead
Calvin Klein	Ellesse
Hugo Boss	Stussy
Bruce Oldfield	Gucci
Jasper Conran	Gianni Versace

PUZZLE 158

Complete the square with the letters of B R Y A N. When completed no row, column or diagonal line will contain the same letter more than once. One horizontal line will spell the name correctly. What letter should replace the question mark?

Answer see page 138

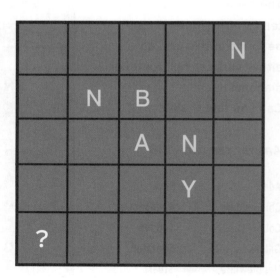

If the country United States is

♈ ♌ ☿ ♓ ♅ ♃   ♑ ♓ ☉ ♓ ♅ ♑

Which are these states?

1.
6.
1.
5.
4.
2.

Answer see page **138**

PUZZLE 160

What is yellow worth?

Answer see page **138**

If the word Presidents is

Who are the other Presidents?

1.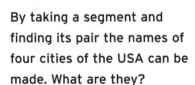

2.

3.

4.

5.

Answer see page 139

PUZZLE 162

By taking a segment and finding its pair the names of four cities of the USA can be made. What are they?

Answer see page 139

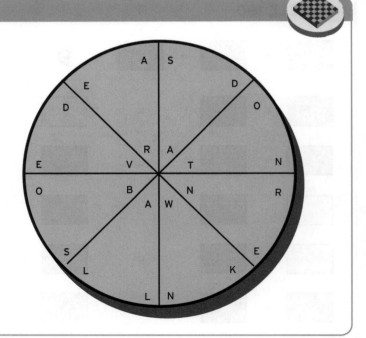

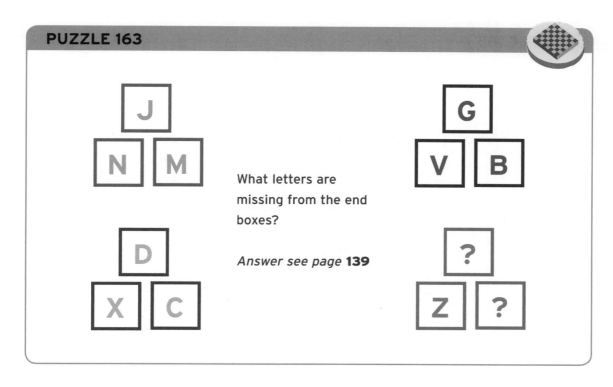

What letters are missing from the end boxes?

Answer see page **139**

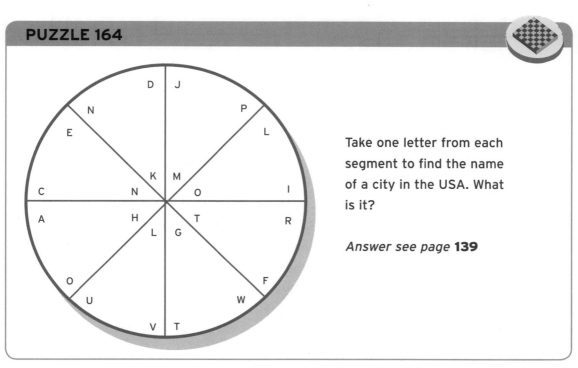

Take one letter from each segment to find the name of a city in the USA. What is it?

Answer see page **139**

FINISH

START

The maze above contains four names of actors and actresses. Find four separate routes through the maze without any route crossing another, although they may merge. On each route collect six letters only to give you the names of the four actors and actresses.

*Answer see page **139***

PUZZLE 166

Take one letter from each segment to find the name of a Canadian city. What is it?

Answer see page **139**

PUZZLE 167

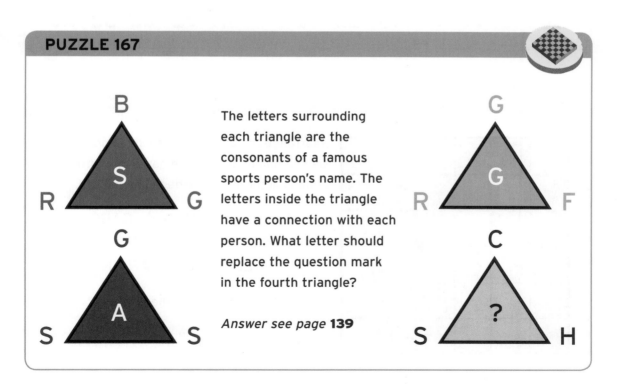

The letters surrounding each triangle are the consonants of a famous sports person's name. The letters inside the triangle have a connection with each person. What letter should replace the question mark in the fourth triangle?

Answer see page **139**

PUZZLE 168

This word frame, when filled with the correct letters, will give the name of a tennis player. The letters are arranged in the coded square on the right. There are two possible alternatives to fill each square of the word frame, one correct, the other incorrect. Who is the tennis player?

Answer see page **139**

	A	B	C	D	E
1	N	W	I	O	M
2	R	C	G	D	A
3	H	F	Y	L	V
4	S	A	L	C	E
5	T	K	E	P	H

1E	4A	3C	3A	1D	5C	3D		4D	1D	4C	1A	4E
5C	1C	2B	2D	4B	2E	5B		1A	5E	2E	3B	2C

PUZZLE 169

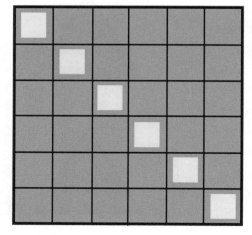

Rearrange the order of these six famous actors' second names to give the name of another famous actor in the shaded diagonal line.

Steve MARTIN, Andy GARCIA, Gary COOPER, Eddie MURPHY, Keanu REEVES, Lee MARVIN.

Who is the actor given in the diagonal?

Answer see page **139**

PUZZLE 170

If the name WOODROW WILSON is

⊘ ⊕ ⊕ ⊘ ⊖ ⊕ ⊘   ⊘ ⊘ ⊕ ⊗ ⊕ ⊖

Who are the other U.S. Presidents?

Answer see page **139**

1. ⊘ ⊘ ⊕ ⊕   ⊖ ⊕ ⊘ ⊖ ⊗ ⊕ ⊖

2. ⊘ ⊘ ⊖ ⊘ ⊖ ⊘ ⊖   ⊕ ⊕ ⊕ ⊖ ⊘ ⊕ ⊕

3. ⊘ ⊗ ⊕ ⊖ ⊘ ⊗   ⊘ ⊘ ⊗ ⊖ ⊘ ⊖ ⊕ ⊕ ⊗ ⊕ ⊖

4. ⊖ ⊘ ⊖ ⊖ ⊘   ⊗   ⊘ ⊖ ⊗ ⊖ ⊘ ⊖

5. ⊘ ⊕ ⊖ ⊖   ⊕   ⊖ ⊗ ⊖ ⊖ ⊗ ⊘ ⊗

6. ⊘ ⊕ ⊖ ⊗ ⊗ ⊗ ⊗   ⊘   ⊘ ⊖ ⊘ ⊖ ⊗

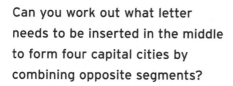

PUZZLE 171

Can you work out what letter needs to be inserted in the middle to form four capital cities by combining opposite segments?

Answer see page **139**

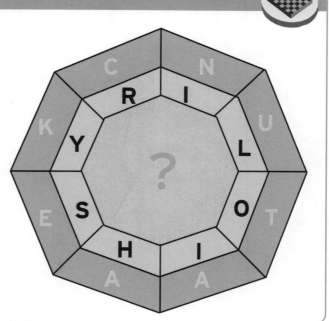

Medium Answers

ANSWER 134

R	N	B	L	F	K	X	C	D	R
E	N	D	C	W	Q	H	S	O	E
N	E	G	A	W	S	K	L	O	V
A	O	H	J	K	O	L	B	P	O
U	R	G	V	D	S	F	Y	J	R
L	T	C	A	R	A	U	G	A	J
T	I	T	O	E	G	U	E	P	M
P	C	Y	T	O	Y	O	T	A	B
J	C	F	V	G	Z	C	W	D	K
E	K	D	P	M	H	Q	G	Y	F

ANSWER 135

i) Yul Brynner ii) Cary Grant iii) Clark Gable iv) Keanu Reaves v) Tony Curtis.

ANSWER 136

The stars are: Tom Cruise, Mel Gibson, Robert De Niro, Steve Martin, Whoopi Goldberg, and Jane Fonda.

O 45	T 32	E 11	S 16	I 47	O 30	T 1	I 14
M 10	O 17	P 46	S 31	L 12	B 15	G 48	R 29
E 33	O 44	G 55	N 58	D 51	N 62	G 13	O 2
N 18	E 52	B 61	O 61	R 54	A 57	I 28	O 49
H 43	V 34	E 59	J 56	D 63	L 50	M 3	T 24
S 8	R 19	A 64	E 53	F 60	D 25	R 38	N 27
E 35	W 42	B 21	U 6	A 37	I 40	R 23	C 4
O 20	I 7	M 36	N 41	E 22	R 5	E 26	T 39

ANSWER 137

Huron, Erie, Apal, Baykal, Cha, Onega, Eyre, Erne, Neagh, Volta, Geneva.

ANSWER 138

The golfers are: Arnold Palmer, Nick Faldo, Tom Watson, Nick Price and Gary Player.

O 23	P 44	C 33	A 8	O 21	R 42	N 31
K 34	A 1	T 22	Y 43	I 32	P 7	D 20
L 45	M 24	L 9	R 12	C 15	N 30	A 41
R 2	P 35	I 14	Y 47	M 10	L 19	D 6
W 25	A 46	E 11	K 16	N 13	G 40	O 29
R 36	N 3	E 48	T 27	C 38	L 5	A 18
R 49	A 26	I 37	O 4	F 17	S 28	E 39

ANSWER 139

Odin, Hermes, Osiris, Poseidon, Athena, Cupid.

ANSWER 140

A. India, China, Delta, Pan Am.

ANSWER 141

i) Einstein ii) Celsius iii) Newton iv) Copernicus v) Pascal vi) Darwin.

ANSWER 142

S	I	A	N	A	S	I	A	N	A
A	P	D	G	H	F	P	J	C	R
F	C	E	G	I	R	A	M	A	A
A	F	H	L	D	J	R	K	F	S
R	Y	Q	U	L	Z	I	Z	R	M
I	R	N	Z	X	B	S	F	X	A
Q	E	V	K	W	O	O	Y	J	S
B	H	K	V	D	W	C	U	G	I
O	B	S	E	S	S	I	O	N	G
R	O	I	D	S	S	I	M	C	D

ANSWER 143

Holly Hunter, Sally Field, Daryl Hannah, Meg Ryan, Demi Moore, Winona Ryder, Jane Fonda, Bette Davis.

MEDIUM ANSWERS

ANSWER 144

N. Monet, Rodin, Munch, Ernst.

ANSWER 145

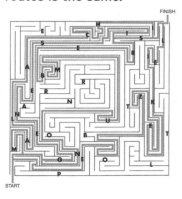

ANSWER 146

Spitz, Borg, Bowe, Lewis, Ali, Pele, Zico, Senna, Lauda, Bats, David, Coe.

ANSWER 147

Albany, Austin, Dallas, Boston
The first letter of two of the routes is the same and the last letter of two of the routes is the same.

ANSWER 148

i) Roberto Baggio ii) Dennis Bergkamp
iii) Kevin Keegan iv) Eric Cantona
v) Jurgen Klinsmann.

ANSWER 149

Zeus

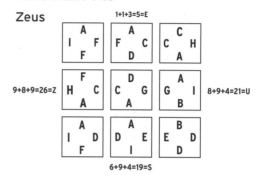

ANSWER 150

Edison, Darwin, Euclid, Pascal.
The first letter of two of the routes is the same and the last letter of two of the routes is the same.

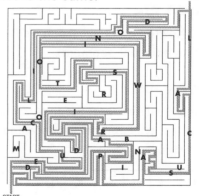

ANSWER 151

Chicago.

ANSWER 152

12. The number of letters between the alphanumeric position of the first and last letters of each name.

ANSWER 153

Rococo, Rubato, Sonata, Timbre.
The first letter of two of the routes is the same and the last letter of two of the routes is the same.

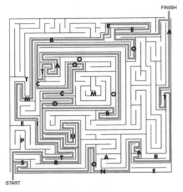

ANSWER 154

Darwin, Newton and Pascal can be found by pairing adjacent segments.

ANSWER 155

The famous writers are: Stephen King, Oscar Wilde, William Shakespeare and Jane Austen.

A 27	E 6	W 17	N 42	S 29	K 8	L 19
R 16	N 49	M 28	N 7	I 18	E 43	H 30
H 5	I 26	A 41	R 38	P 35	D 20	I 9
E 48	A 15	E 36	S 1	J 40	A 31	A 44
L 25	P 4	E 39	S 34	A 37	N 12	E 21
C 14	T 47	T 2	I 23	O 12	U 45	K 32
E 3	L 24	S 13	S 46	E 33	W 22	G 11

ANSWER 156

T	R	Y	J	P	Q	X	G	D	H	K	X
M	A	D	N	V	R	K	F	Z	F	W	Z
J	R	N	O	D	D	E	S	Y	J	O	T
P	S	N	O	T	A	R	E	H	S	Z	F
C	H	E	P	P	L	E	W	H	I	T	E
H	C	H	I	P	P	E	N	D	A	L	E
D	M	B	Y	Z	H	I	S	C	P	G	J
F	T	A	G	W	F	T	L	Y	I	B	M
X	U	K	D	D	U	O	D	L	N	T	X
M	V	C	P	A	C	K	L	W	I	G	K
K	W	G	R	K	M	O	V	R	U	H	Y
Z	H	T	R	X	W	W	B	N	Y	K	P

ANSWER 157

Y	N	J	Z	B	W	K	X	B	T	N	F	G
G	I	O	R	G	I	O	A	R	M	A	N	I
T	E	S	S	O	B	O	G	U	H	R	G	A
X	L	V	E	S	V	R	Y	C	R	N	B	N
R	K	Q	S	H	F	X	B	E	V	O	K	N
Z	N	G	S	W	L	J	D	O	Q	C	M	I
J	I	T	E	M	P	O	F	L	W	R	Q	V
Y	V	K	L	K	R	S	B	D	Z	E	S	E
W	L	N	L	D	B	H	P	F	Q	P	D	R
F	A	T	E	G	U	C	C	I	X	S	Y	S
X	C	A	L	T	P	Q	M	E	H	A	W	A
V	D	G	J	V	Z	D	Y	L	G	J	Z	C
S	T	U	S	S	Y	F	K	D	B	J	B	E

ANSWER 158

Y.

B	R	Y	A	N
A	N	B	R	Y
R	Y	A	N	B
N	B	R	Y	A
Y	A	N	B	R

ANSWER 159

i) Minnesota ii) Texas iii) Alaska
iv) California v) Florida vi) Louisiana.

ANSWER 160

7.

ANSWER 161

Carter, Eisenhower, Johnson, Reagan, Roosevelt.

ANSWER 162

Boston, Dallas, Denver and Newark can be found by pairing opposite segments.

ANSWER 163

ANSWER 164

Portland.

ANSWER 165

Turner, Kilmer, Taylor, Gibson.
The first letter of two of the routes is the same, and the last letter of three of the routes is the same.

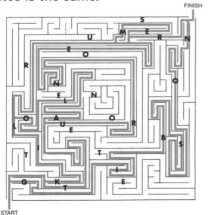

ANSWER 166

Winnipeg.

ANSWER 167

A. The letters outside are consonants of famous tennis players. They are: (top) Borg and Graf, (bottom) Agassi and Cash. The letters inside the triangles are the initials of their nationality. They are Swedish, German, American and Australian respectively.

ANSWER 168

Michael Chang.

ANSWER 169

Tony Curtis.

C	O	O	P	E	R
M	U	R	P	H	Y
M	A	R	V	I	N
M	A	R	T	I	N
G	A	R	C	I	A
R	E	E	V	E	S

ANSWER 170

i) Bill Clinton ii) Abraham Lincoln
iii) George Washington iv) Harry S. Truman v) John F. Kennedy vi) Ulysses Grant.

ANSWER 171

O. Cairo, Hanoi, Seoul, Tokyo.

Difficult Puzzles

Prepare to really feel your mind sweat! The puzzles in this section have all been carefully devised to push your mental functions to the absolute maximum. There are no easy solutions here, no quick gimmes – just lots and lots of really good, seriously challenging problems to test your capabilities. You'll need to use every trick you've learned to master the brain-benders in these pages – and you'll have to draw on some serious resolve and creativity, to boot.

But if the difficulty level of these problems is set to high, then so is the reward. The puzzles in this section are the ones that will really help you build new mental muscle. By stretching yourself beyond the point of everyday comfort, you are forced to strengthen and grow. That's as true of the mind as it is of the body. In a gym, these puzzles would be the final two or three extra-heavy lifts – the ones that do you as much good (or more) as all the workouts that went before them.

That's not all, either. These puzzles are a real challenge, and that means that solving them is a real achievement. As you work through the problems in this section, you'll feel the deep satisfaction of genuinely proving yourself against a serious obstacle. Every one you beat will become a badge of pride – another item to add to the stack of things you can feel good about. And that's every bit as important as the really great mental exercise you'll be doing. Play on: mind fitness awaits!

Find the 10 horse & carriage sets
hidden behind these vehicles.

Answer see page **244**

PUZZLE 173

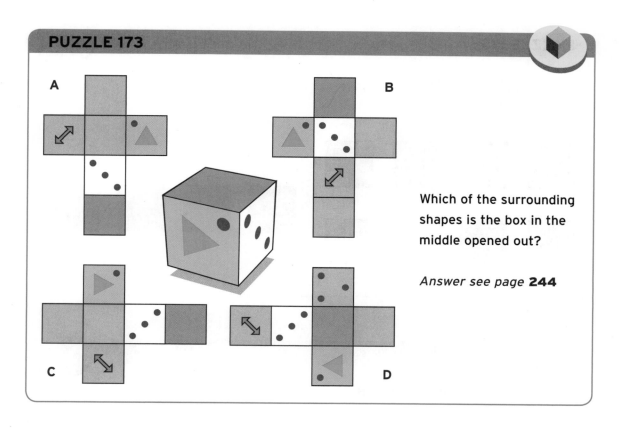

Which of the surrounding shapes is the box in the middle opened out?

*Answer see page **244***

PUZZLE 174

Which of the figures below should replace the question mark in the box?

Answer see page 244

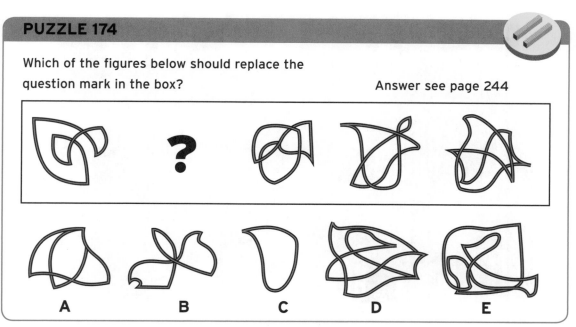

A   B   C   D   E

PUZZLE 175

What should replace the question mark?

Answer see page 244

  ?

A B C D

PUZZLE 176

Find the 14 differences in picture B.

Answer see page 244

A

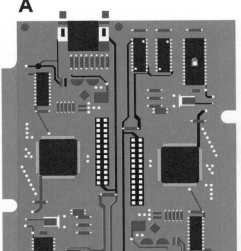

B

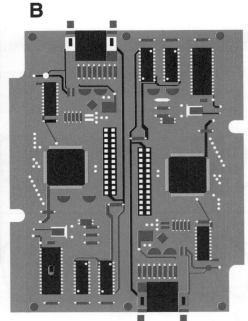

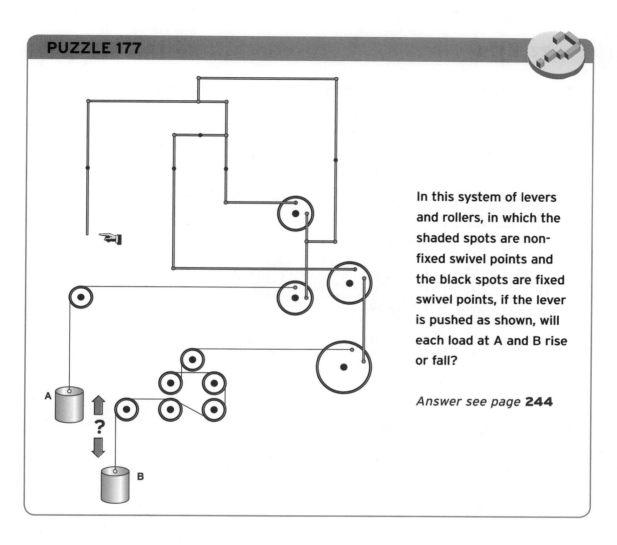

In this system of levers and rollers, in which the shaded spots are non-fixed swivel points and the black spots are fixed swivel points, if the lever is pushed as shown, will each load at A and B rise or fall?

Answer see page **244**

Which of the following is the odd one out?   *Answer see page* **244**

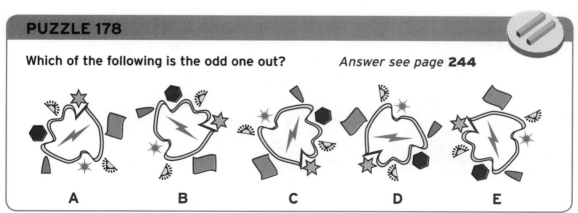

A   B   C   D   E

PUZZLE 179

Which set does not go with the other three?

Answer see page **244**

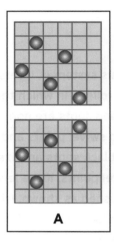 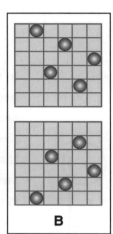 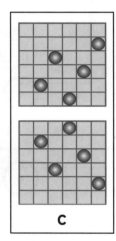 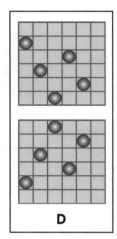

| A | B | C | D |

PUZZLE 180

What comes next in this series?

Answer see page **244**

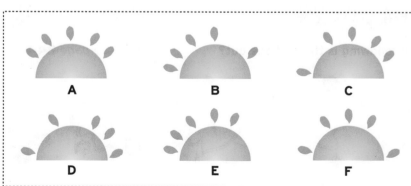

A   B   C

D   E   F

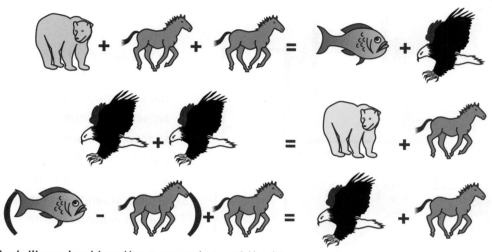

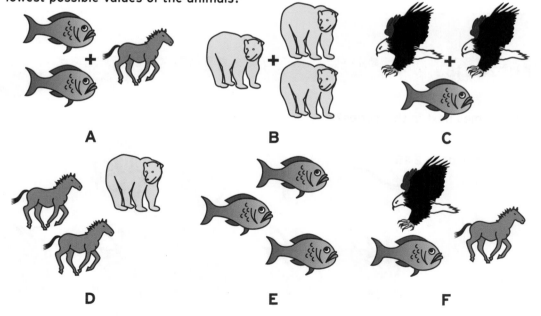

Each like animal has the same value and the bear, horse, fish and bird all have different values. Which of A, B, C, D, E or F is the total value of the single column above the question mark, and what are the lowest possible values of the animals?

?

*Answer see page **244***

PUZZLE 182

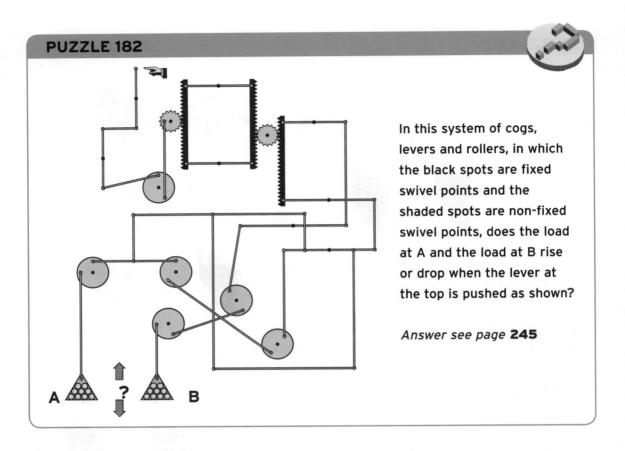

In this system of cogs, levers and rollers, in which the black spots are fixed swivel points and the shaded spots are non-fixed swivel points, does the load at A and the load at B rise or drop when the lever at the top is pushed as shown?

Answer see page **245**

A ? B

PUZZLE 183

What comes next in this series?

Answer see page **245**

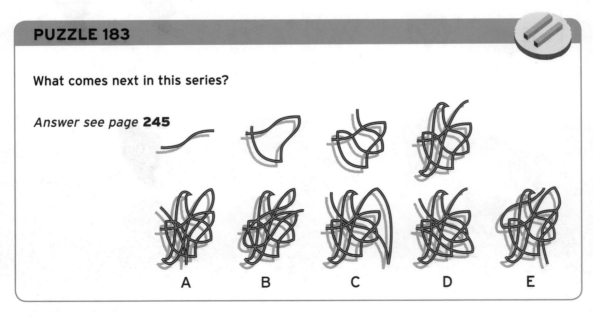

A B C D E

PUZZLE 184

Which of the following is the odd one out?

Answer see page **245**

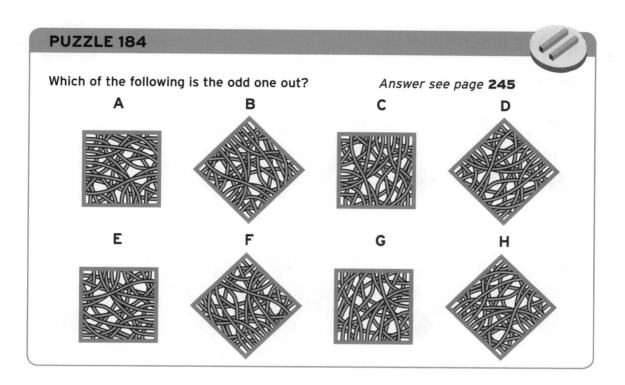

A   B   C   D

E   F   G   H

PUZZLE 185

Which of the following is the odd one out?

Answer see page **245**

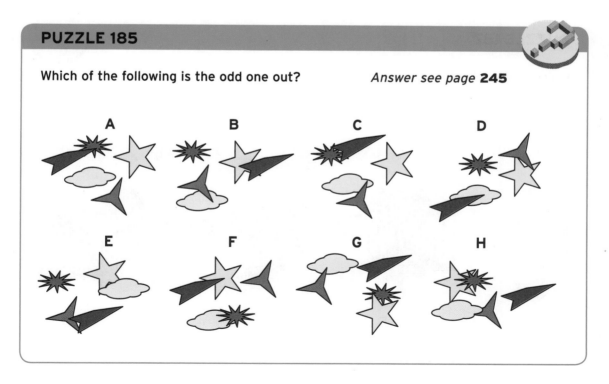

A   B   C   D

E   F   G   H

PUZZLE 186

What comes next in this series?

*Answer see page **245***

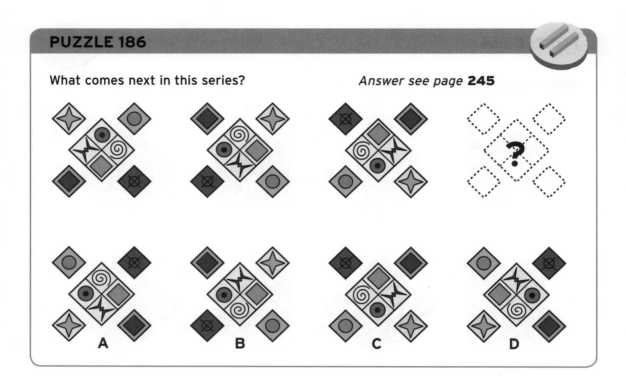

A   B   C   D

PUZZLE 187

Which of the following is the odd one out?

*Answer see page **245***

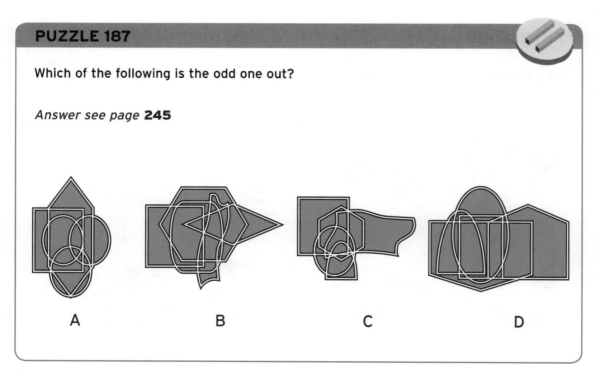

A   B   C   D

Find the odd one out in each row.

Answer see page **245**

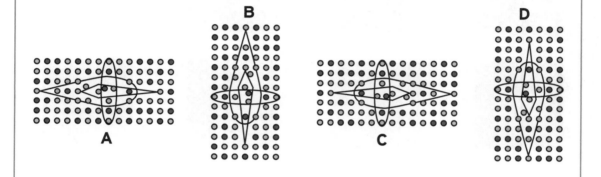

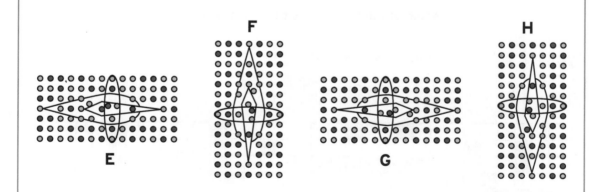

PUZZLE 189

Complete the analogy.

Answer see page **245**

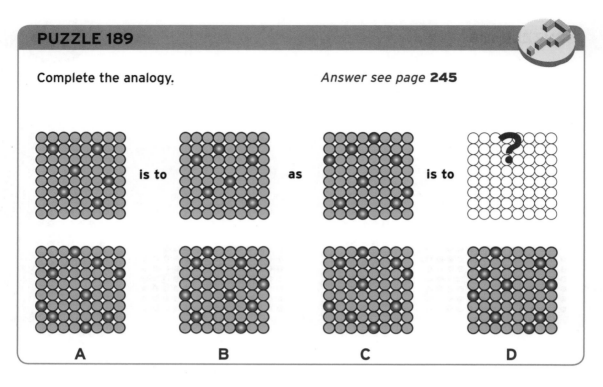

A   B   C   D

PUZZLE 190

Which of the following is the odd one out?

Answer see page **245**

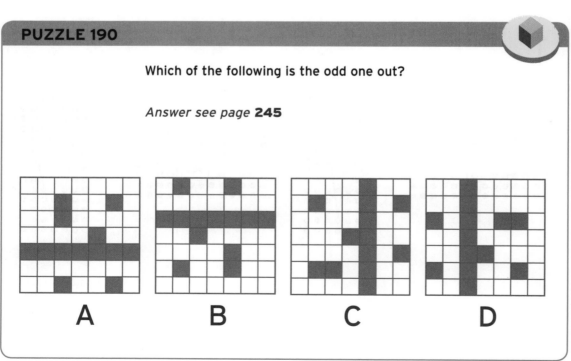

A   B   C   D

PUZZLE 191

Here is a long multiplication sum. Each symbol represents a number from 0 to 9, and each like symbol always represents the same number. With this in mind, which symbol should replace the question mark?

Answer see page 245

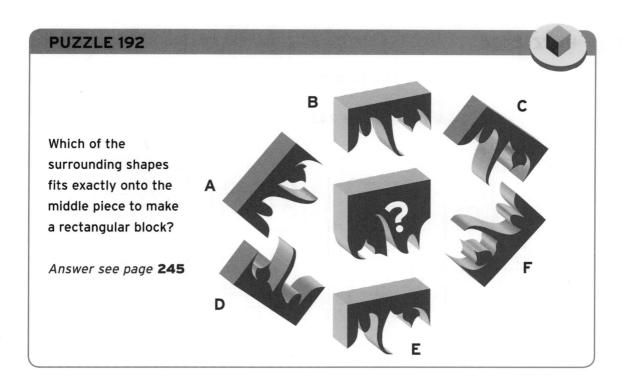

PUZZLE 192

Which of the surrounding shapes fits exactly onto the middle piece to make a rectangular block?

Answer see page 245

PUZZLE 193

In this system of levers and rollers the black spots are fixed swivel points and the shaded spots are non-fixed swivel points. With this in mind, if the lever is pushed as shown, will the load rise or fall?

Answer see page **245**

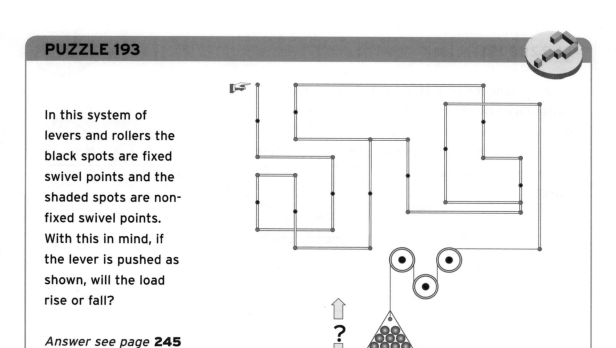

PUZZLE 194

Which of the following is the odd one out?

Answer see page **245**

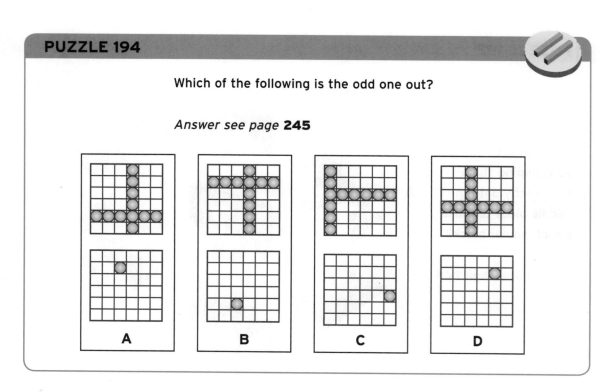

A   B   C   D

PUZZLE 195

Which of the following is the odd one out?

Answer see page **245**

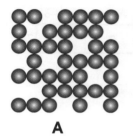 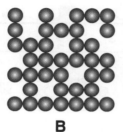  

A   B   C   D

PUZZLE 196

Which is the odd one out in each row?

Answer see page **246**

A   B   C   D

   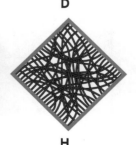

E   F   G   H

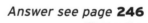

PUZZLE 197

Each like symbol has the same value throughout. What is the missing symbol?
Clue: the small numbers are the totals for each row.

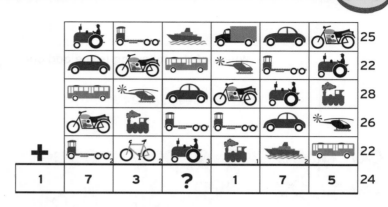

						25
						22
						28
						26
						22
1	7	3	?	1	7	5	24

A   B   C   D   E

F   G   H   I   J

Answer see page 246

PUZZLE 198

258 269 212   237 217 254 268 242   ?

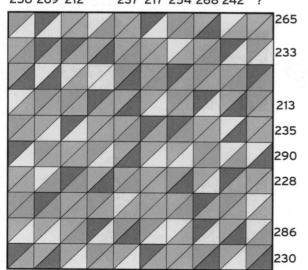

265

233

213

235

290

228

286

230

What number could replace the question mark?

Answer see page 246

PUZZLE 199

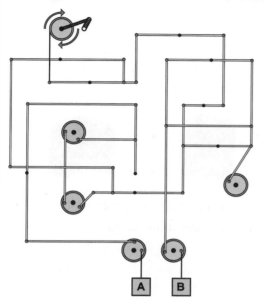

In this system of pulley wheels and levers, where the black spots are fixed pivots and the shaded spots are non-fixed pivots, will (A) rise or fall and will (B) rise or fall when the wheel at the top is turned in the direction indicated?

Answer see page **246**

PUZZLE 200

Which two patterns do not go with the other three?

Answer see page **246**

A   B   C   D   E

Which objects should replace the question marks?

Answer see page **246**

PUZZLE 202

Which of the following is the odd one out?

Answer see page **246**

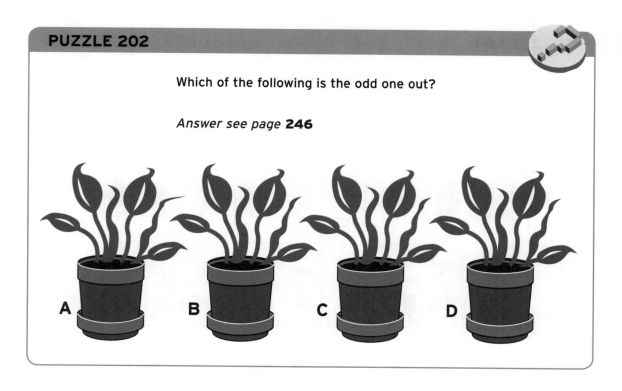

PUZZLE 203

Complete the analogy.

Answer see page **246**

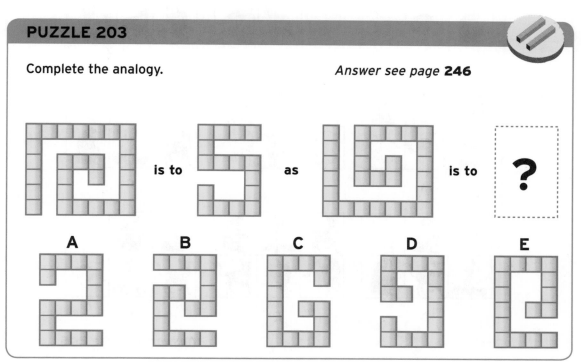

Which set of tiles goes into the middle to
complete the pattern?

Answer see page **246**

PUZZLE 205

Which figure or figures below is or are
identical to the one in the box?

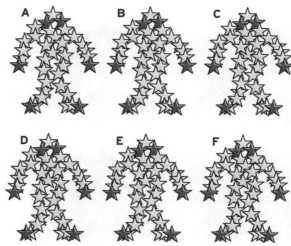

Answer see page **246**

PUZZLE 206

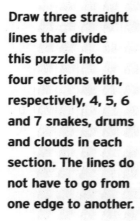

Draw three straight
lines that divide
this puzzle into
four sections with,
respectively, 4, 5, 6
and 7 snakes, drums
and clouds in each
section. The lines do
not have to go from
one edge to another.

Answer see page **246**

PUZZLE 207

Which of the following make three pairs of identical scenes?

A

B

C

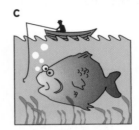

D

E

F

Answer see page **246**

PUZZLE 208

When old gardener Lincoln died, he left his grandchildren 19 rose bushes each. The grandchildren, Agnes (A), Billy (B), Catriona (C) and Derek (D), hated each other, and so decided to fence off their plots as shown. Who had to build the greatest run of fence?

Answer see page **246**

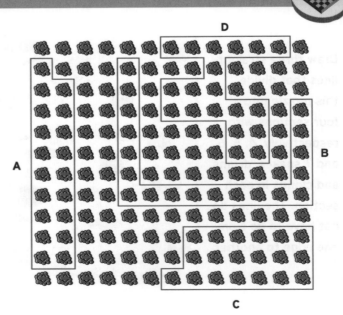

PUZZLE 209

94   98   75   ?

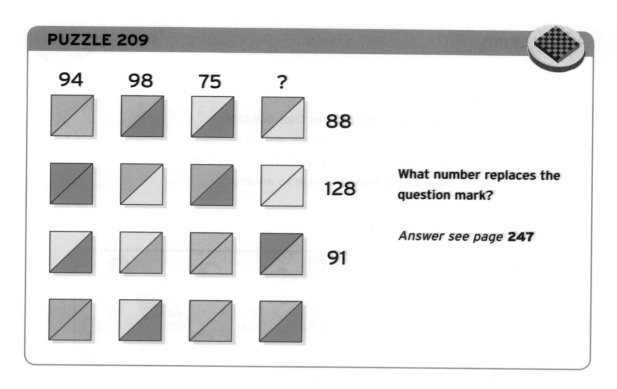

88

128

91

What number replaces the
question mark?

Answer see page **247**

PUZZLE 210

The black dots represent hinge points. If points A and B are moved together, will
points C and D move together or apart?

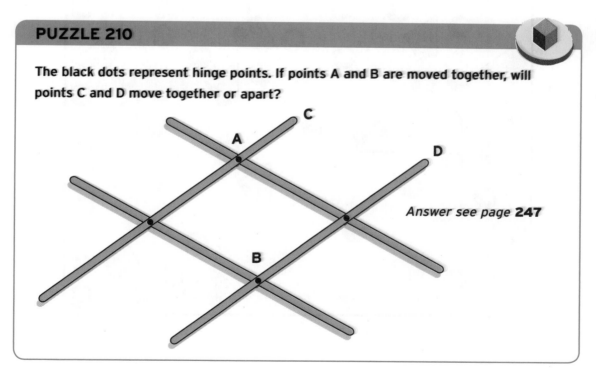

Answer see page **247**

Draw four straight lines that divide this
puzzle into seven sections, with 3 pyramids
and 7 balls in each section. The lines do not
have to go from one edge to another.

Answer see page **247**

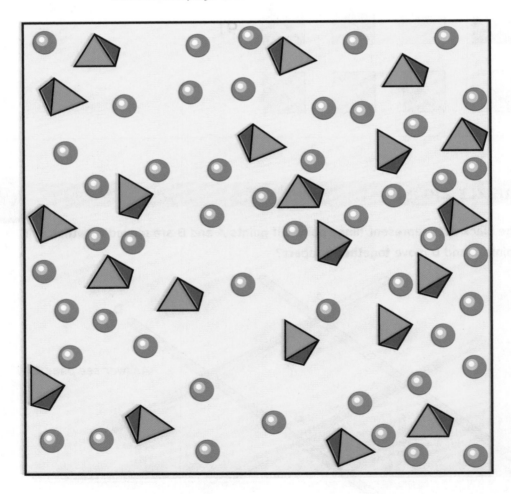

PUZZLE 212

Complete the analogy.

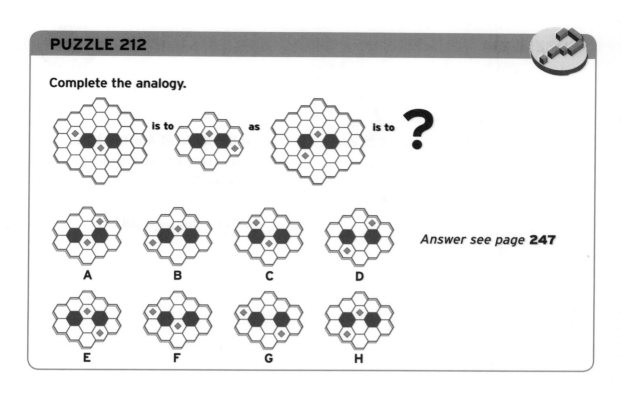

Answer see page **247**

PUZZLE 213

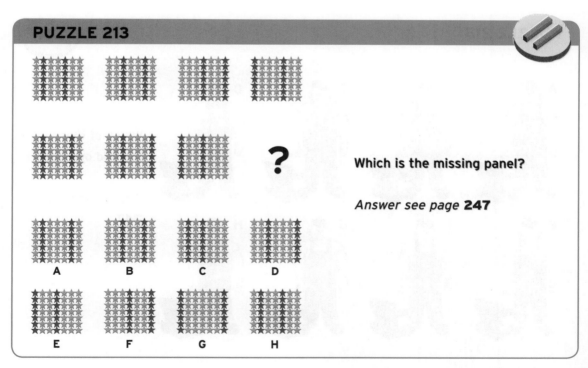

Which is the missing panel?

Answer see page **247**

PUZZLE 214

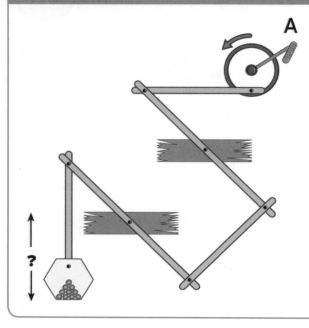

If the wheel at A is turned as indicated, will the load first rise, or fall?

Answer see page **247**

PUZZLE 215

A

B

C

D

Which of these is the odd one out?

Answer see page **247**

E

F

G

H

PUZZLE 216

This system is in balance. The black block weighs the same as the pale blocks. If three more blocks are placed on the black block, where should two pale blocks be placed to return the system to balance?

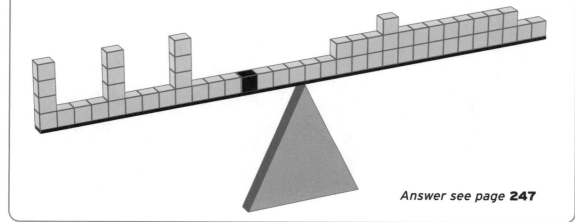

Answer see page **247**

PUZZLE 217

Which letters replace the question mark?   *Answer see page* **247**

B — G C — D H — B C — D

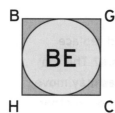 BE   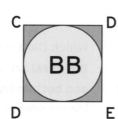 BB   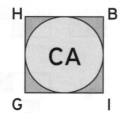 CA   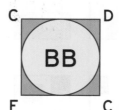 BB

H — C D — E G — I F — C

H — I D — A B — F H — F

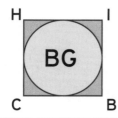 BG   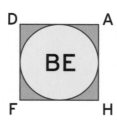 BE   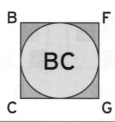 BC   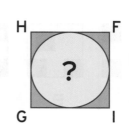 ?

C — B F — H C — G G — I

Which of the following is the odd one out?

Answer see page **247**

A 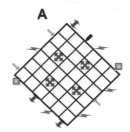 B 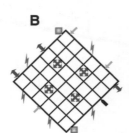 C 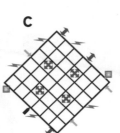 D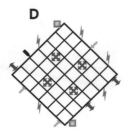

Which tile should replace the question mark? The top and bottom boxes may move independently of each other.

Answer see page **247**

A   B   C   D

PUZZLE 220

```
77  80  79  86  77     76  84  78  ?
```

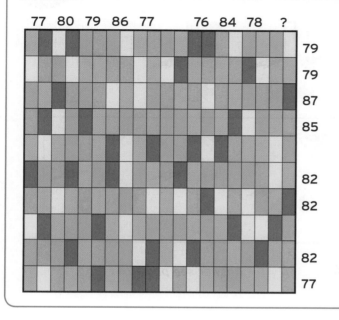

79
79
87
85

82
82

82
77

What number could replace the
question mark?

Answer see page **247**

PUZZLE 221

Which of the following is the odd one out?

Answer see page **247**

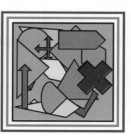

A   B   C   D

PUZZLE 222

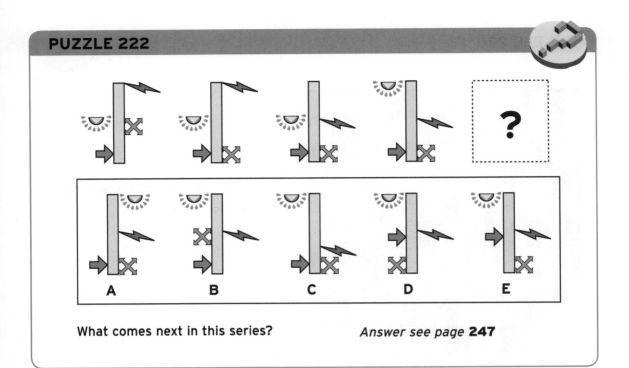

What comes next in this series?

Answer see page **247**

PUZZLE 223

Which panel should replace the question mark?

Answer see page **247**

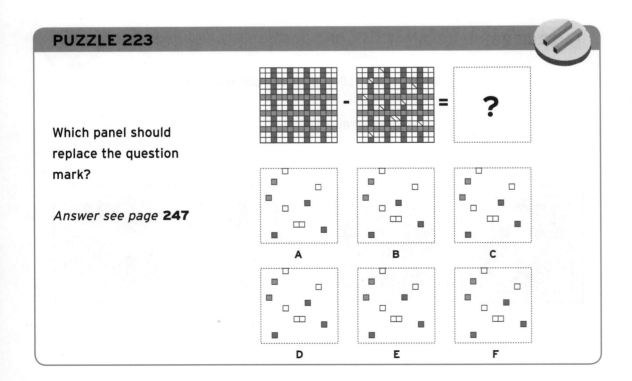

PUZZLE 224

In this system of cogs, levers and pulley wheels, in which the black spots are fixed pivot points and the shaded spots are non-fixed pivot points, the loads at A and B are in balance. Which one will rise when the wheel at the bottom is turned as indicated?

Answer see page 247

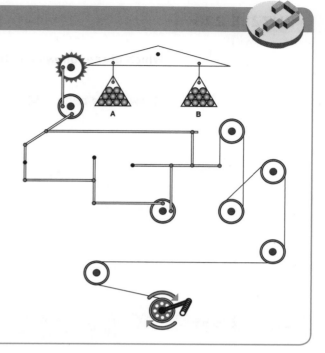

PUZZLE 225

Complete the analogy.

Answer see page 247

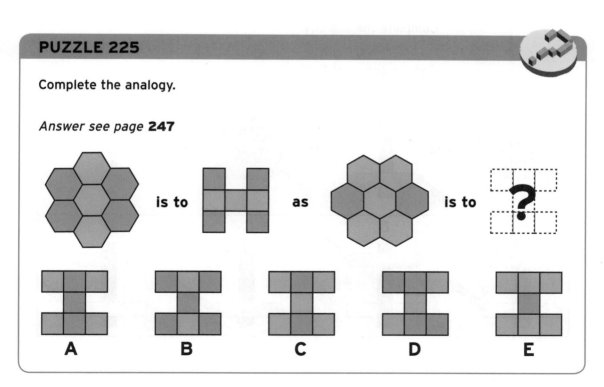

A   B   C   D   E

PUZZLE 226

Which of the following is the odd one out?

Answer see page **248**

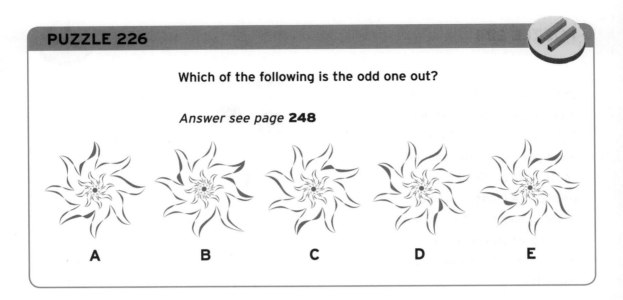

A   B   C   D   E

PUZZLE 227

Complete the analogy.

Answer see page **248**

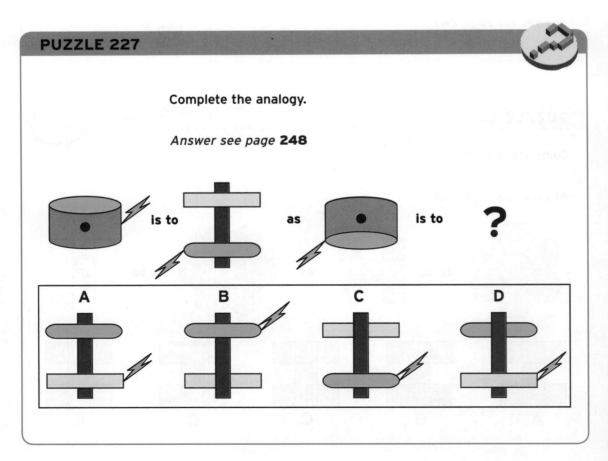

is to   as   is to   ?

A   B   C   D

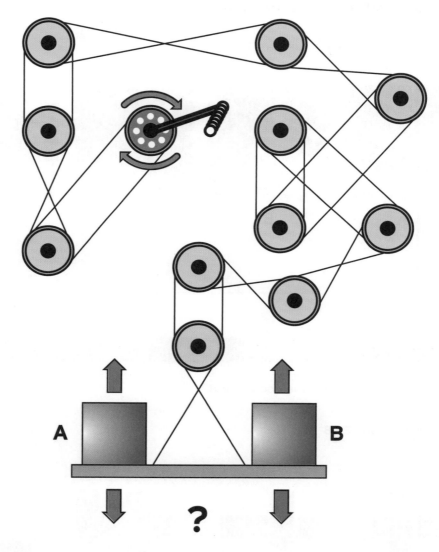

A

B

?

What will happen when the
pedal turns?

Answer see page **248**

Which of the following is the odd one out?

Answer see page **248**

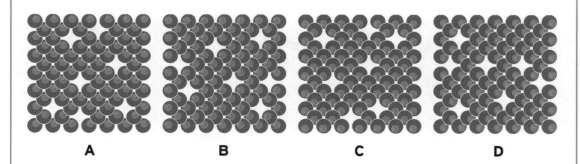

| A | B | C | D |

Which of the following is the odd one out?

Answer see page **248**

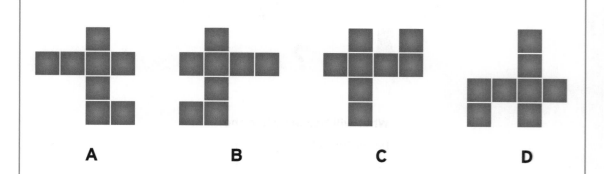

| A | B | C | D |

If a brick is dropped from the top of a cliff (on a planet with no atmosphere) at the same time that a projectile is fired parallel with the ground from a large gun, will:

(a) they reach the ground together?
(b) the brick land first?
(c) the projectile land first?

Answer see page **248**

PUZZLE 232

Complete the analogy.

Answer see page 248

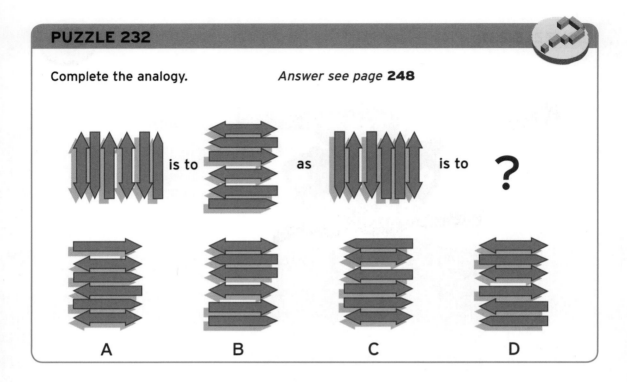

A   B   C   D

PUZZLE 233

What comes next in this series?

Answer see page 248

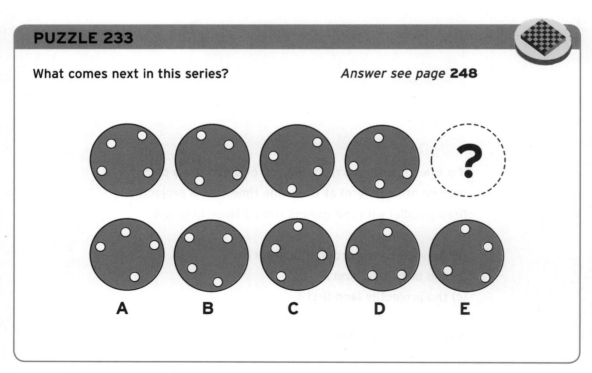

A   B   C   D   E

PUZZLE 234

Which set of shapes fits into the middle of this panel to complete the pattern?

Answer see page **248**

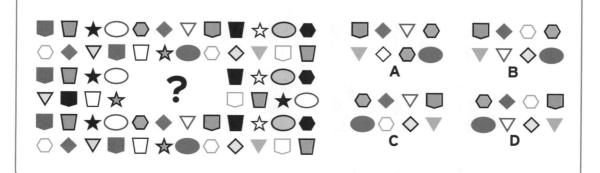

PUZZLE 235

Complete the analogy.

Answer see page **248**

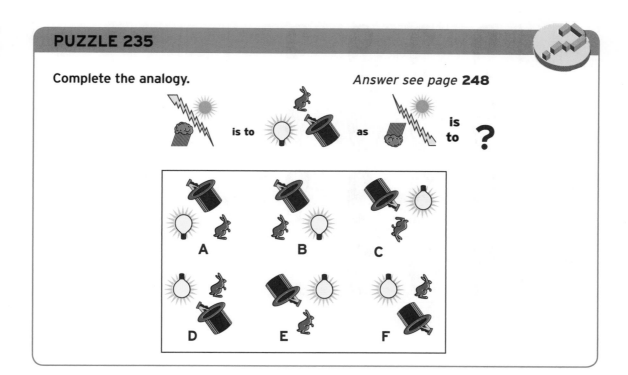

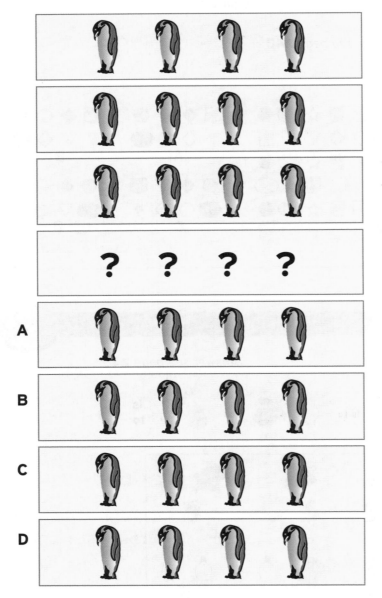

Which tile comes next in this series?

Answer see page **248**

PUZZLE 237

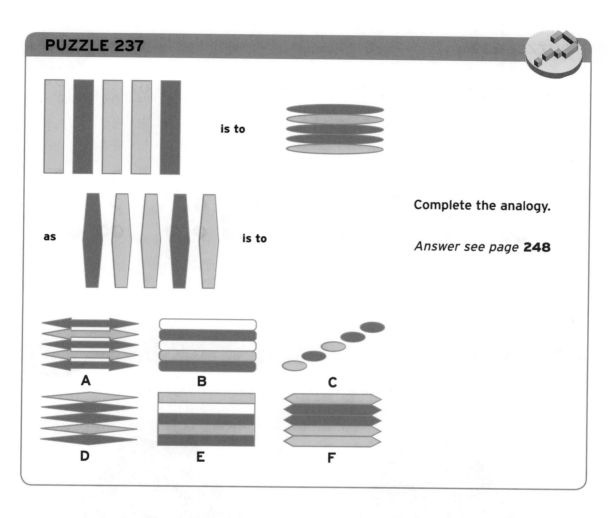

is to

as

is to

Complete the analogy.

Answer see page **248**

A   B   C

D   E   F

PUZZLE 238

Which of the following is the odd one out?

Answer see page **248**

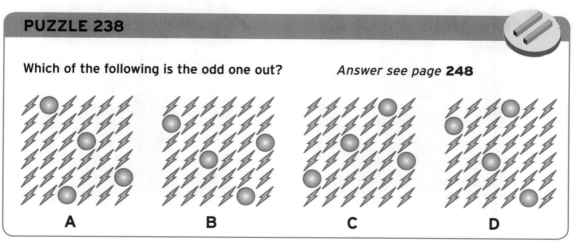

A   B   C   D

PUZZLE 239

Find the two shapes that don't go with the other three.

Answer see page **248**

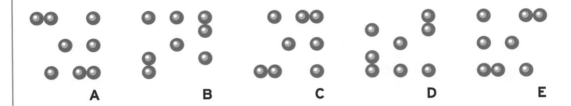

| A | B | C | D | E |

PUZZLE 240

Mark the 12 differences in picture B.

Answer see page **248**

A

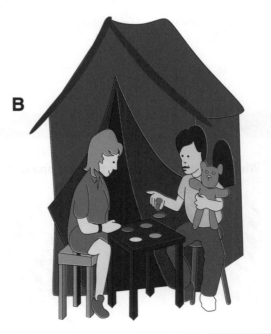

B

Complete the analogy.

Answer see page **248**

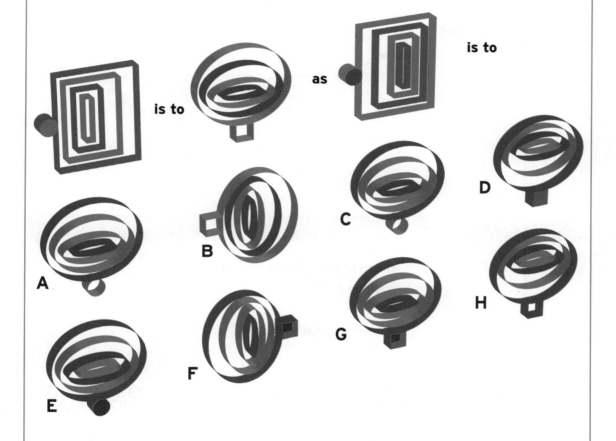

PUZZLE 242

Shade in this map of the USA Midwest using no more than 4 tints, so that no adjacent borders have the same hue.

Answer see page **249**

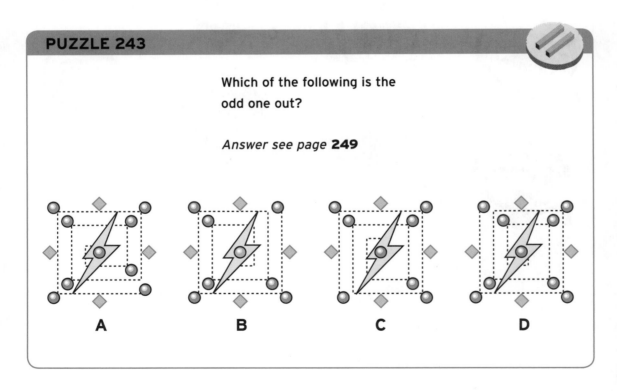

PUZZLE 243

Which of the following is the odd one out?

Answer see page **249**

A   **B**   **C**   **D**

PUZZLE 244

If the black arrow pulls in the direction indicated, will the load rise or fall?

Answer see page **249**

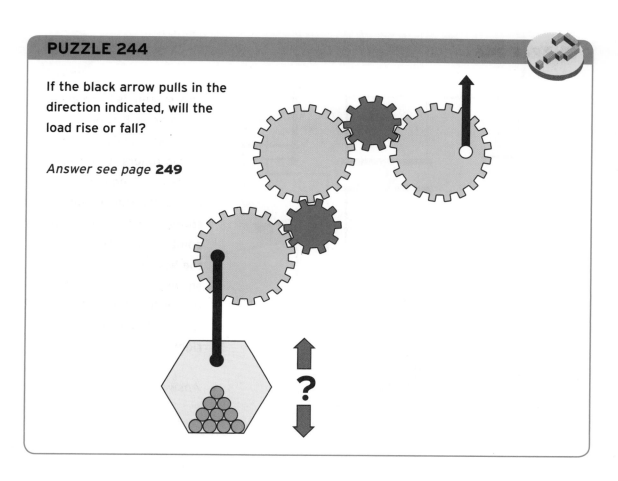

PUZZLE 245

Which of the following is the odd one out?

Answer see page **249**

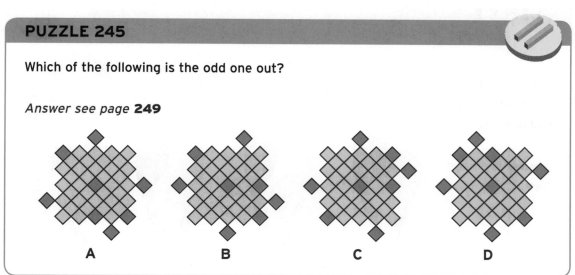

A   B   C   D

PUZZLE 246

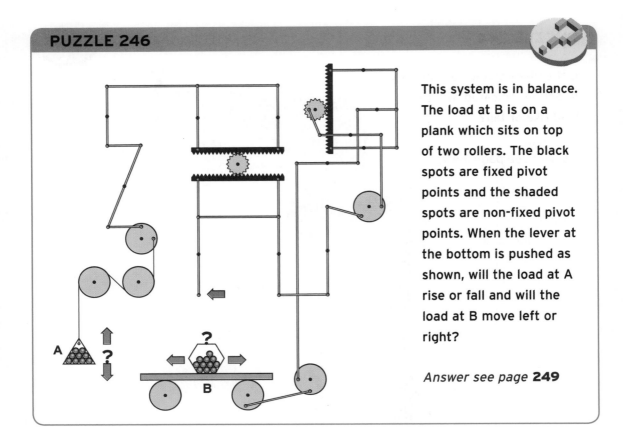

This system is in balance. The load at B is on a plank which sits on top of two rollers. The black spots are fixed pivot points and the shaded spots are non-fixed pivot points. When the lever at the bottom is pushed as shown, will the load at A rise or fall and will the load at B move left or right?

Answer see page **249**

PUZZLE 247

Which of these penguins is the odd one out?

Answer see page **249**

A   B   C   D

PUZZLE 248

Which of the following is the odd one out?

Answer see page **249**

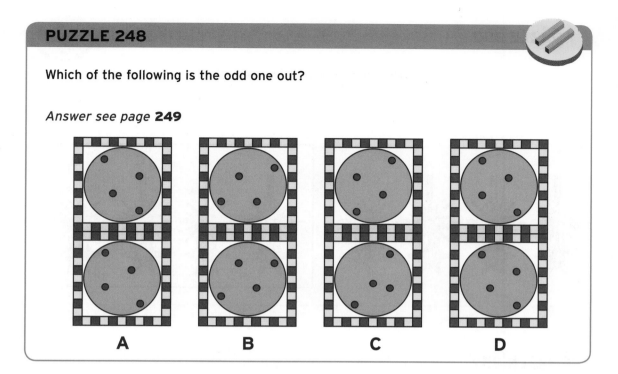

A **B** **C** **D**

PUZZLE 249

Which number replaces the question mark?

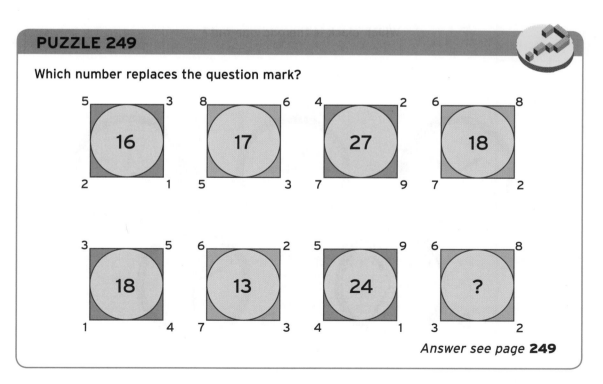

Answer see page **249**

PUZZLE 250

What comes next in this series?

Answer see page **249**

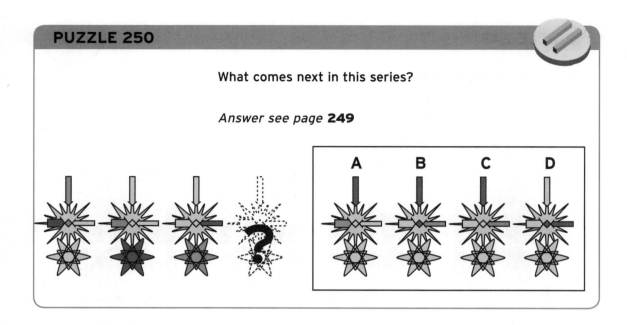

PUZZLE 252

Which clock is the odd-one-out?

Answer see page **249**

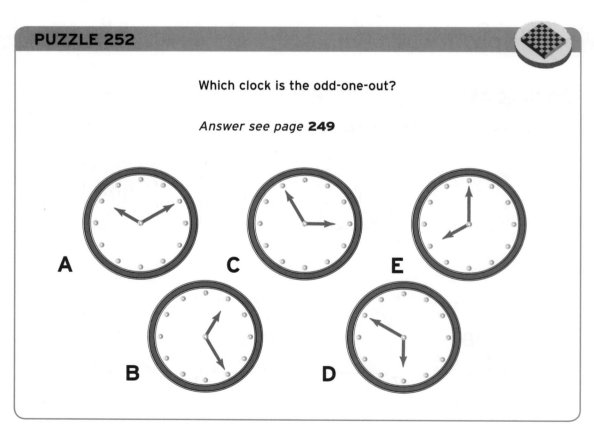

PUZZLE 252

Which of the following is the odd one out?

Answer see page **249**

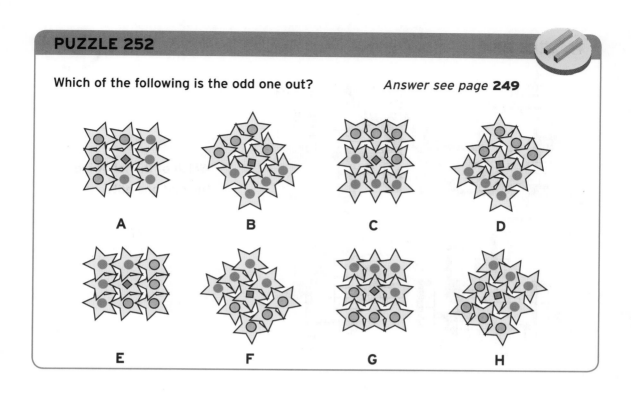

A   B   C   D

E   F   G   H

PUZZLE 253

Find the 14 differences in picture B.

Answer see page **249**

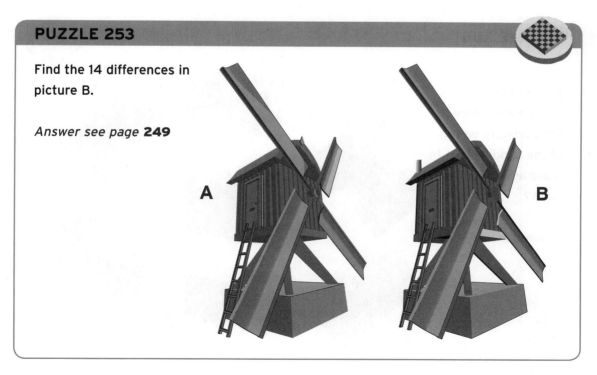

A   B

PUZZLE 254

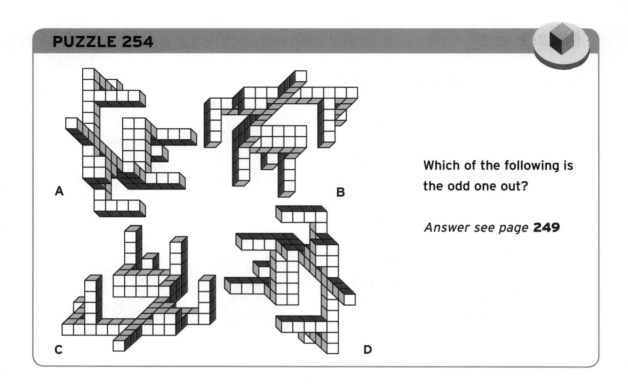

A

B

C

D

Which of the following is the odd one out?

Answer see page **249**

PUZZLE 255

Which of the surrounding pieces fits perfectly on top of the middle piece to make a rectangular block?

Answer see page **249**

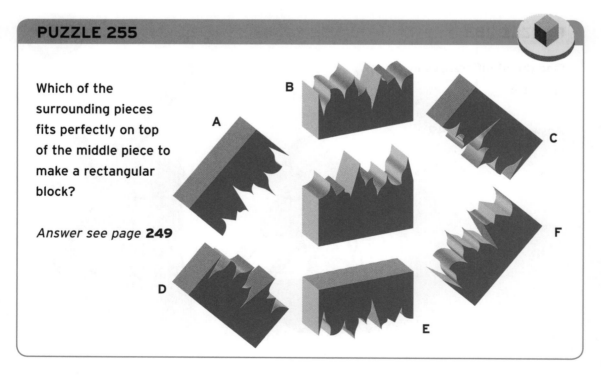

A

B

C

D

E

F

PUZZLE 256

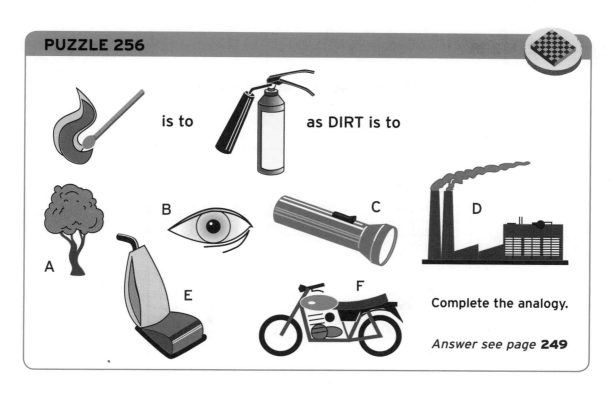

is to ... as DIRT is to

Complete the analogy.

Answer see page **249**

PUZZLE 257

What comes next in this series?

Answer see page **249**

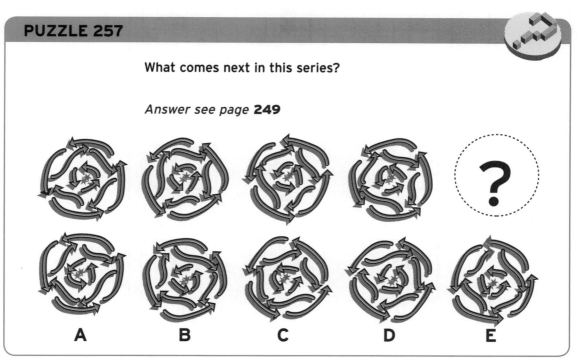

A B C D E

PUZZLE 258

Which tile is missing from the following panel?

Answer see page **249**

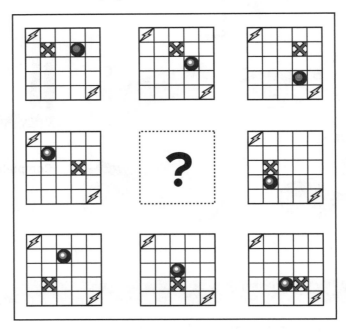

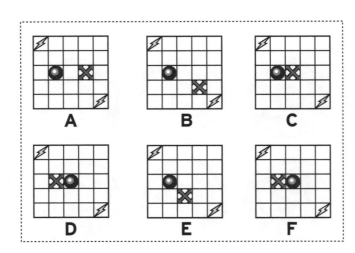

A   B   C

D   E   F

90 ●●●

PUZZLE 259

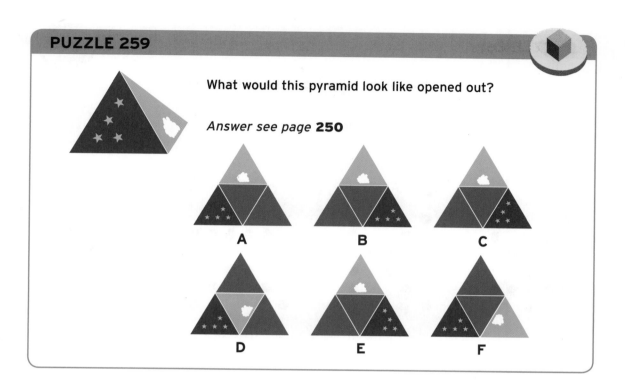

What would this pyramid look like opened out?

Answer see page **250**

PUZZLE 260

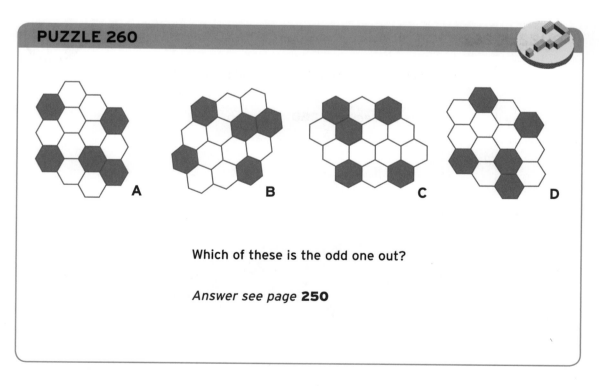

Which of these is the odd one out?

Answer see page **250**

PUZZLE 261

Which of the following is the odd one out?

Answer see page **250**

A   **B**   **C**   **D**

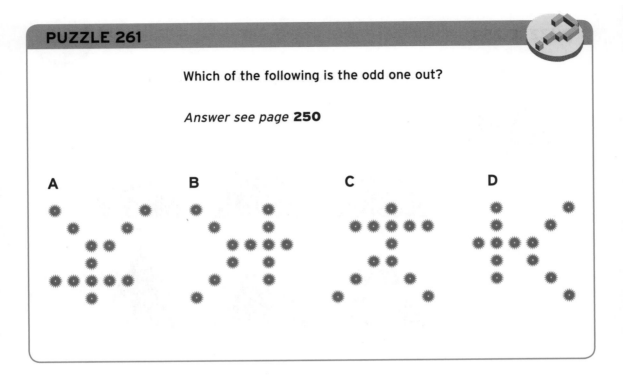

PUZZLE 262

Which of the following is the odd one out?

Answer see page **250**

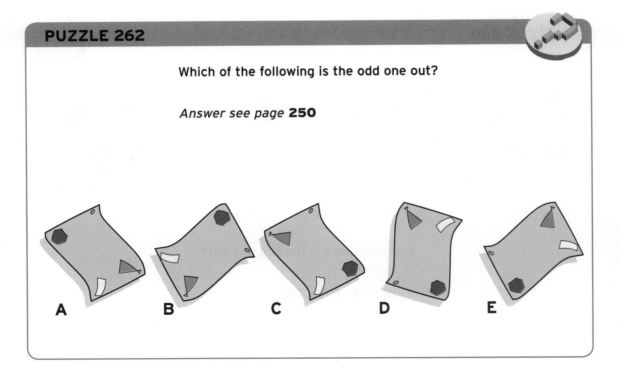

A   **B**   **C**   **D**   **E**

PUZZLE 263

Which of the following is the odd one out?

Answer see page **250**

A

B

C

D

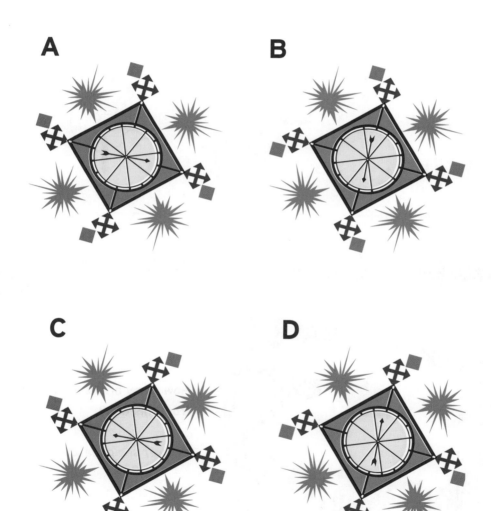

PUZZLE 264

Which of the following is
the odd one out?

Answer see page **250**

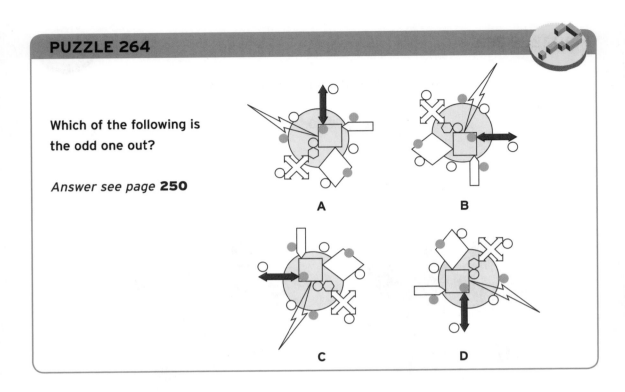

A

B

C

D

PUZZLE 265

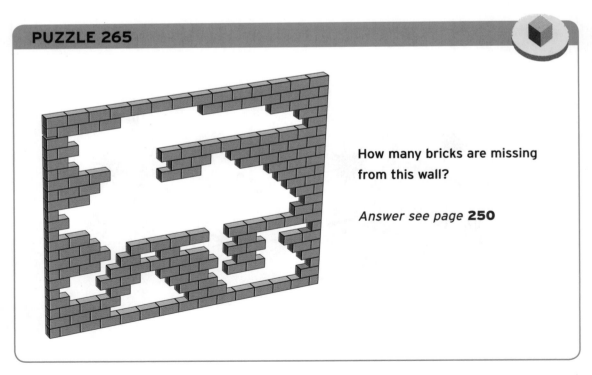

How many bricks are missing
from this wall?

Answer see page **250**

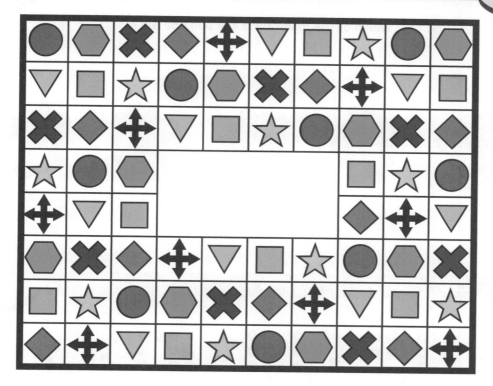

A

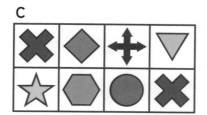

B

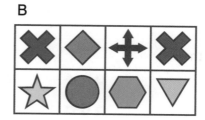

C

D

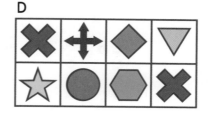

Which panel fills the gap?

Answer see page **250**

PUZZLE 267

Which of the following is the odd one out?

Answer see page **250**

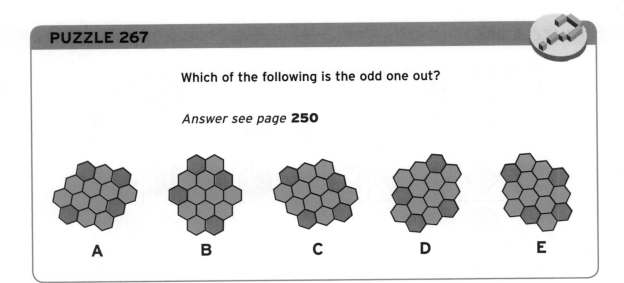

A   B   C   D   E

PUZZLE 268

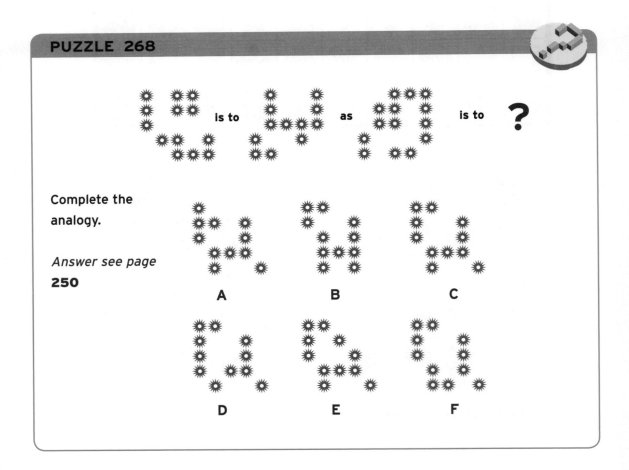

is to ___ as ___ is to **?**

Complete the
analogy.

Answer see page
250

A   B   C

D   E   F

Which jet fighter is missing?

Answer see page **250**

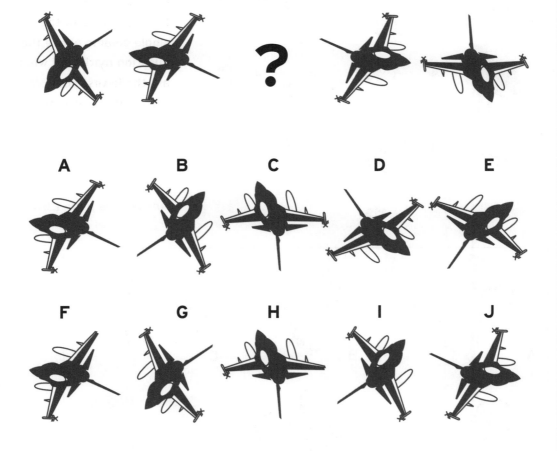

Each like animal has the same value and the leopard, flea, dog and rabbit all have different values. Which of A, B, C, D, E or F is the total value of the single column above the question mark, and what are the lowest possible values of the animals?

Answer see page **250**

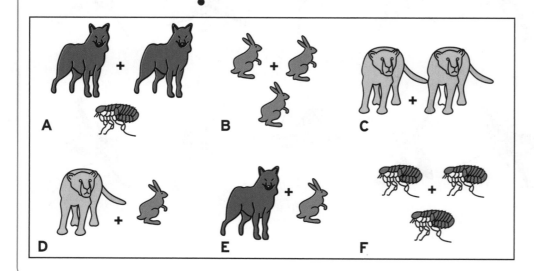

Which is the missing set?

Answer see page **250**

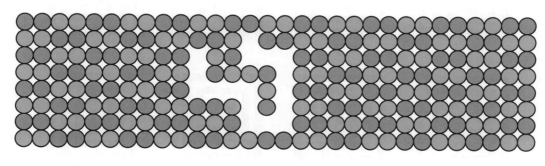

A	B	C	D

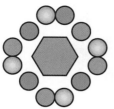 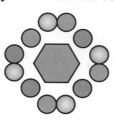 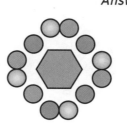 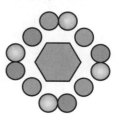

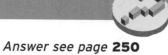

Which of the following is the odd one out?   *Answer see page* **250**

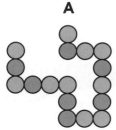 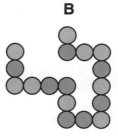 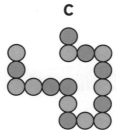 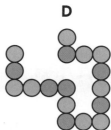

A   **B**   **C**   **D**

PUZZLE 273

Which is the odd one out?

Answer see page **250**

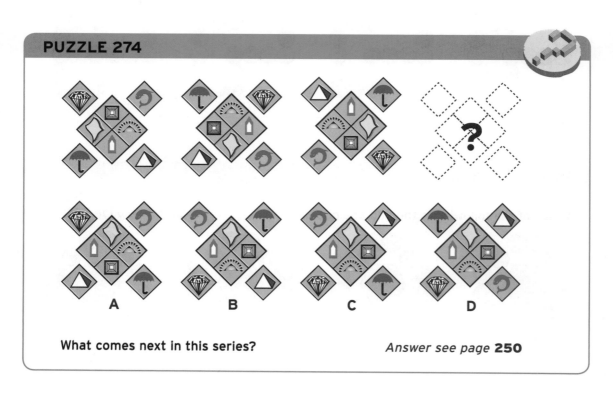

A   B   C   D

E   F   G   H

PUZZLE 274

A   B   C   D

What comes next in this series?

Answer see page **250**

PUZZLE 275

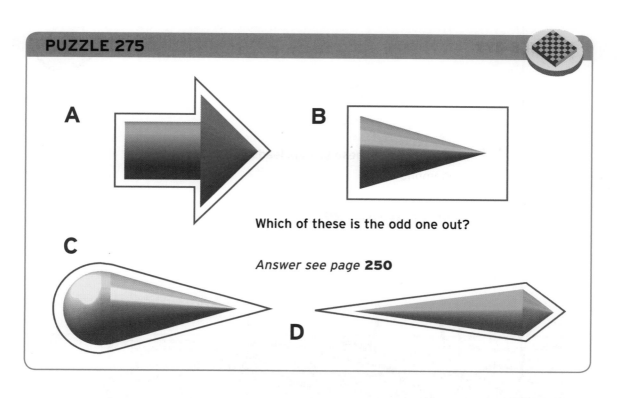

A

B

Which of these is the odd one out?

Answer see page **250**

C

D

PUZZLE 276

What comes next?

Answer see page **251**

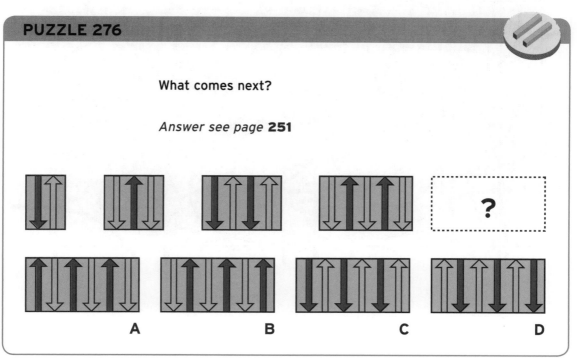

A   B   C   D

Which one of these strings leads you to the diamond?

Answer see page **251**

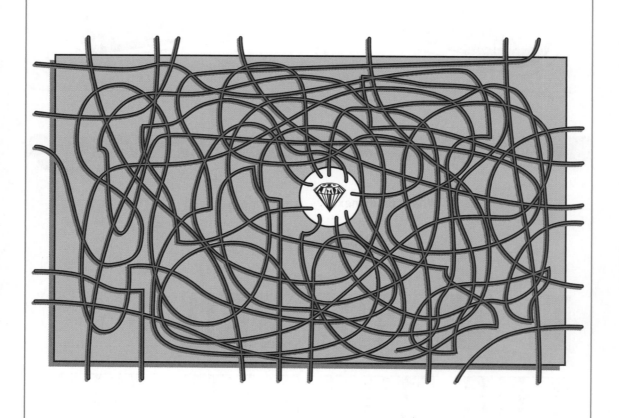

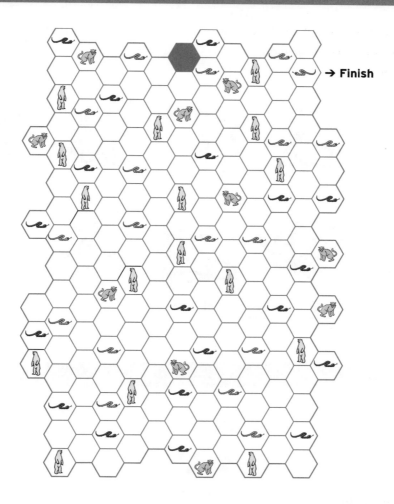

→ **Finish**

As park ranger on this safari you have to collect as many rattlesnakes as possible without getting killed or maimed by them or other creatures. The wildcats will eat a part of your body if you step onto a sector which they have scent-marked and the bears will hug you to death. The bears and wildcats have marked one segment next to the one they stand on, but you have no way of knowing which one. You may not go back over your tracks. Start on the shaded sector and finish on the snake facing the other way.

Answer see page **251**

PUZZLE 279

Which two of these form an identical pair that do not go with the other eight?

Answer see page **251**

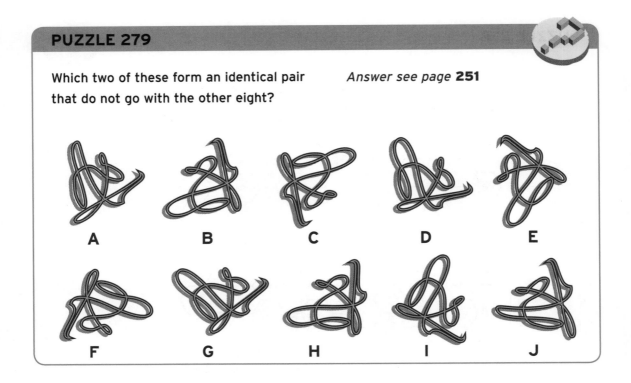

PUZZLE 280

Which pattern can be used to make the box in the middle?

Answer see page **251**

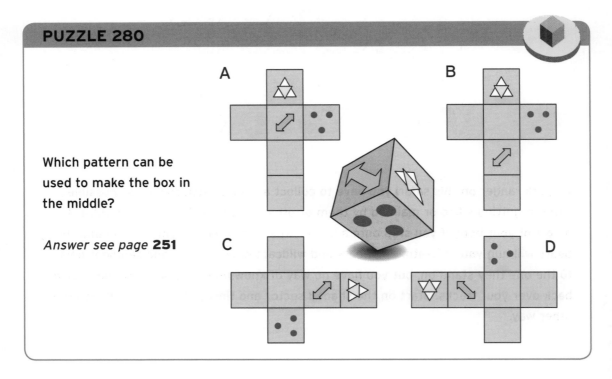

PUZZLE 281

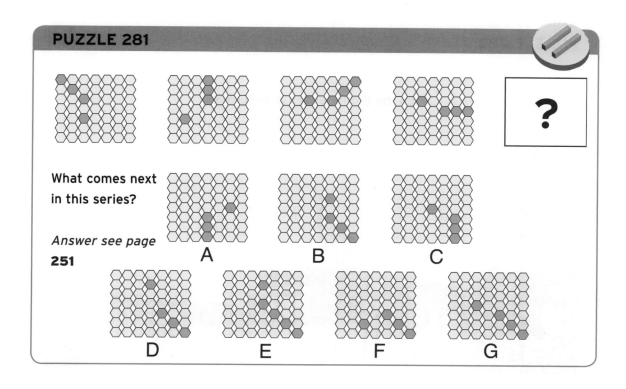

What comes next in this series?

Answer see page **251**

A   B   C

D   E   F   G

PUZZLE 282

Which of the following is the odd one out?

Answer see page **251**

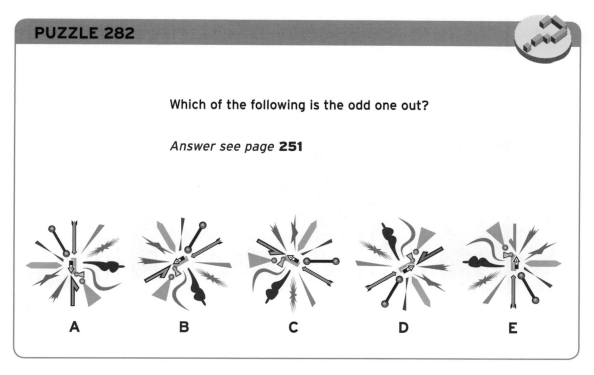

A   B   C   D   E

Find the 8 differences in picture B.

Answer see page **251**

A

B

PUZZLE 284

What number replaces the question mark?   *Answer see page* **251**

99   69   87   137   ?

PUZZLE 285

Which of the following is the odd one out?

Answer see page **251**

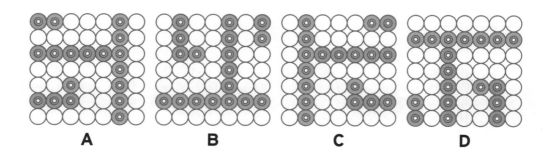

A   B   C   D

PUZZLE 286

Which of the following is the odd one out?

Answer see page **251**

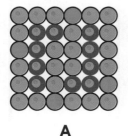 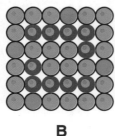  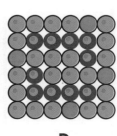

| A | B | C | D |

PUZZLE 287

Which two birds are identical?

Answer see page **251**

A   B   C   D

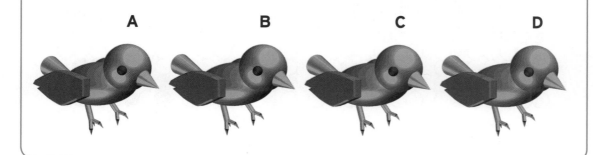

PUZZLE 288

Which of the following is the odd one out?

Answer see page **251**

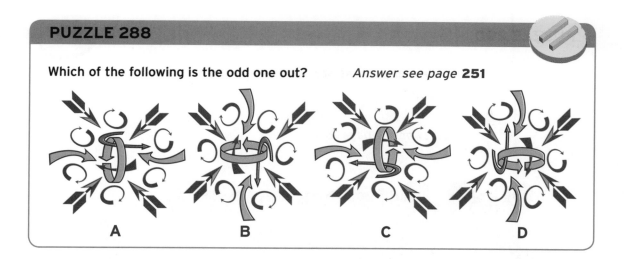

A   B   C   D

PUZZLE 289

Draw four straight lines that divide this puzzle into five sections with 1 scuba diver, 3 fish and respectively, 4, 5, 6, 7 and 8 large bubbles and sea shells in each section. The lines do not have to go from one edge to another.

Answer see page **252**

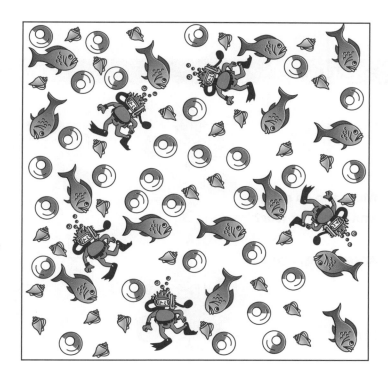

PUZZLE 290

How many cobras are in this menacing group?

Answer see page **252**

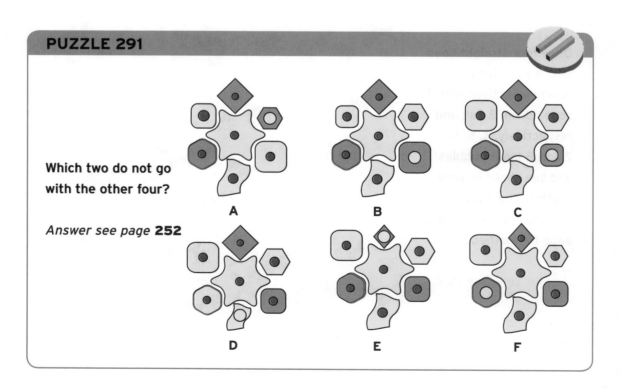

PUZZLE 291

Which two do not go with the other four?

Answer see page **252**

A

B

C

D

E

F

PUZZLE 292

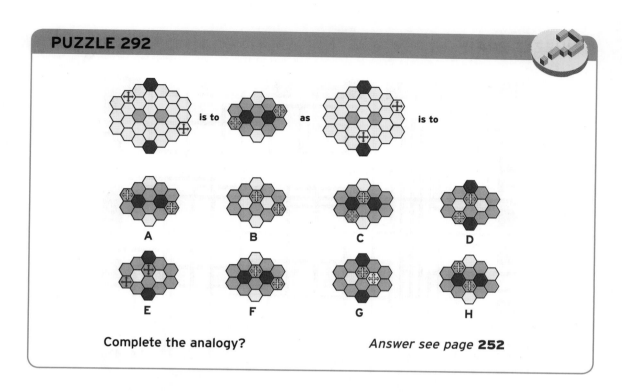

Complete the analogy?

Answer see page **252**

PUZZLE 293

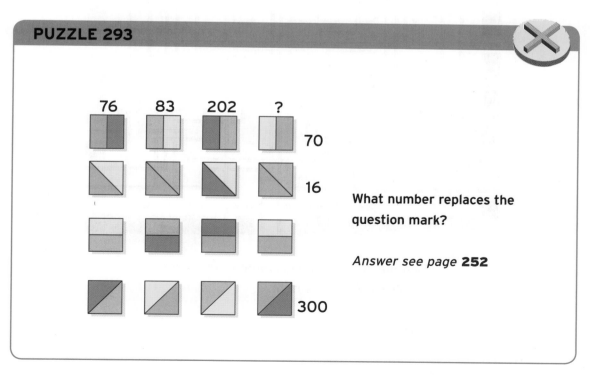

76   83   202   ?

70

16

What number replaces the question mark?

Answer see page **252**

300

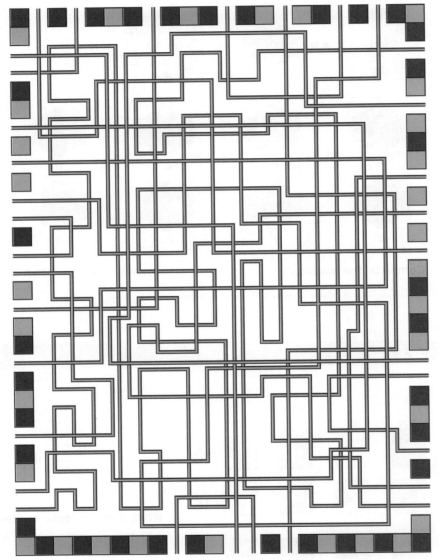

Find the only continuous route from the left
of this puzzle to the right.

Answer see page **252**

PUZZLE 295

Draw three straight lines that divide this puzzle into six sections that contain 1 fish and 1 flag in each and respectively 0, 1, 2, 3, 4 and 5 drums and lightning bolts. The lines do not have to go from one edge to another.

Answer see page **252**

PUZZLE 296

Which of the following is the odd one out?

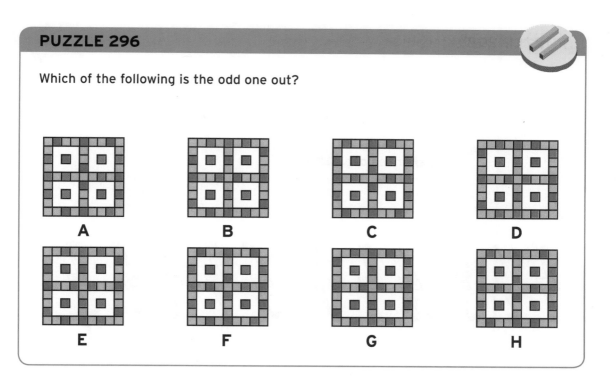

A

B

C

D

E

F

G

H

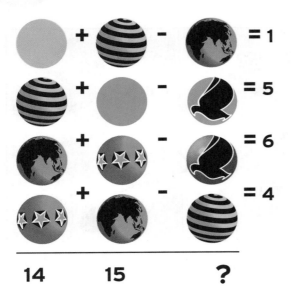

14   15   ?

From the information given, work out the missing total and the values of the different images.

Answer see page **252**

What comes next in this series?

Answer see page **253**

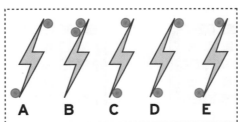

A   B   C   D   E

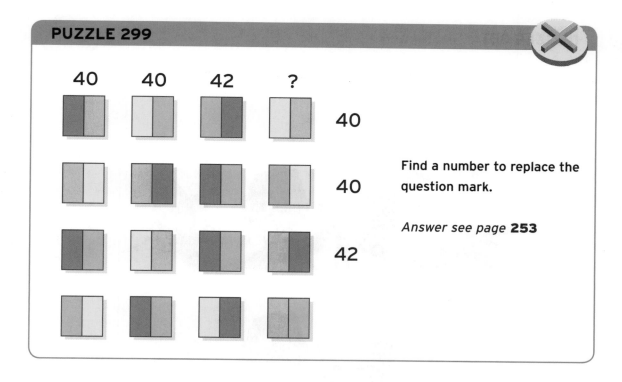

40

40

42

Find a number to replace the
question mark.

Answer see page **253**

What comes next in this series?

Answer see page **253**

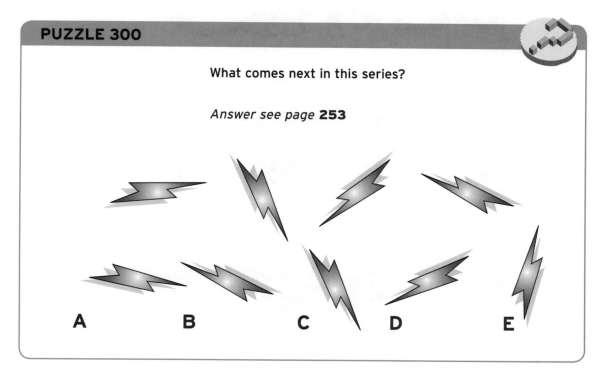

A   B   C   D   E

Which of the following is the odd one out?

Answer see page **253**

A

B

C

D

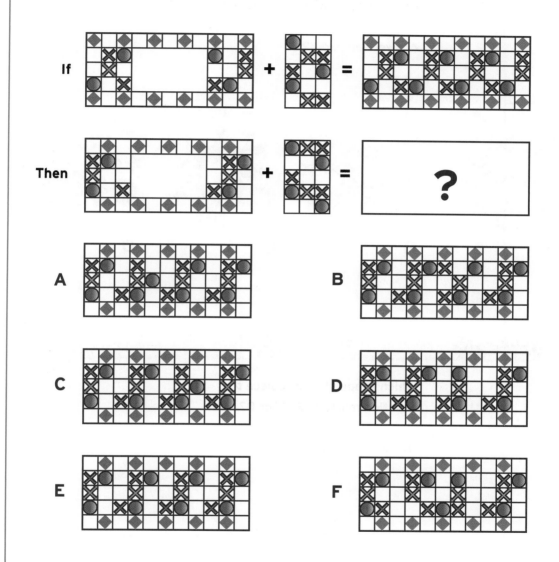

Complete the addition.

Answer see page **253**

PUZZLE 303

Which of the following is the odd one out?

Answer see page **253**

A   **B**   **C**   **D**

PUZZLE 304

Which shape should replace the
question mark, A, B, C, or D?

Answer see page **253**

   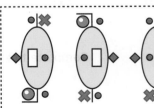

A   **B**   **C**   **D**

PUZZLE 305

Which of the following is the odd one out?

Answer see page **253**

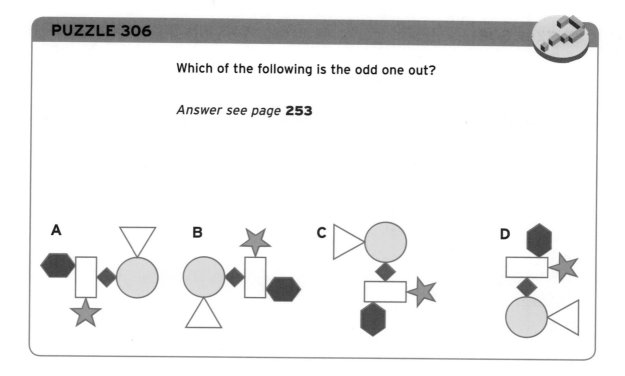

A   B   C   D

PUZZLE 306

Which of the following is the odd one out?

Answer see page **253**

A   B   C   D

PUZZLE 307

Which set fits into the middle of this set of tiles?

Answer see page **253**

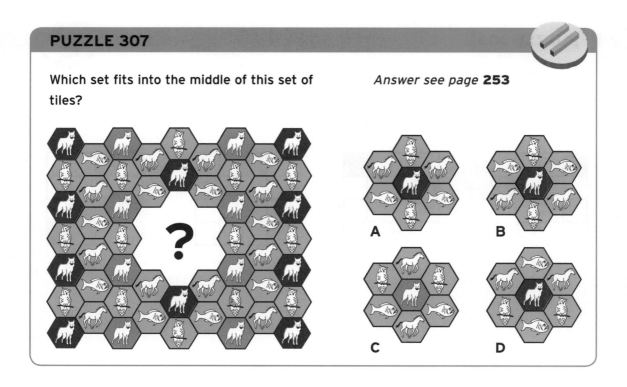

A

B

C

D

PUZZLE 308

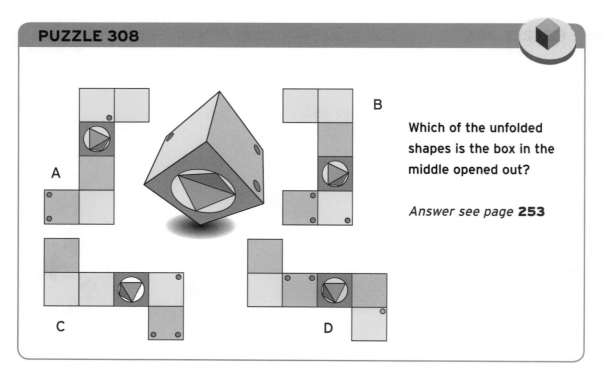

B

Which of the unfolded shapes is the box in the middle opened out?

Answer see page **253**

A

C

D

PUZZLE 309

Complete the analogy.

Answer see page **253**

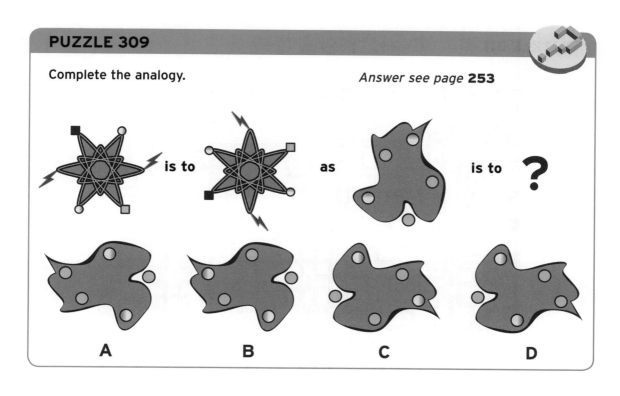

A   **B**   **C**   **D**

PUZZLE 310

Which of the following is the odd one out?

Answer see page **253**

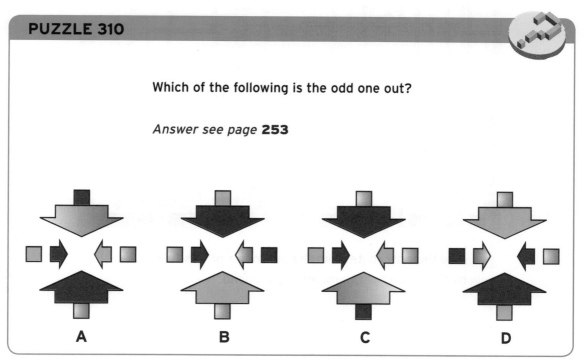

A   **B**   **C**   **D**

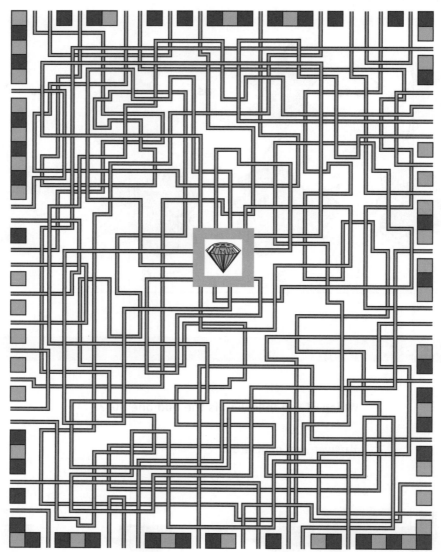

Find the only route from the perimeter of this field
to the shaded path around the diamond.

Answer see page **253**

Draw three straight lines that make four sections with a total value of 40 in each, using the values given below. The lines do not have to go from one edge to another.

Answer see page **253**

0   1   2   3   4   5

PUZZLE 313

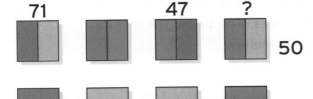

71   47   ?

50

128

48

What number replaces the question mark?

Answer see page **254**

PUZZLE 314

Which 3 of the drums below continue the sequence.

Answer see page **254**

?   ?   ?

A   B   C   D   E   F

Draw five straight lines that divide this puzzle into six sections that have 1 chimp, 1 koala, 3 snakes, 4 dogs and 5 stars in each section. The lines do not have to go from one edge to another.

Answer see page **254**

What comes next in this series?

Answer see page **254**

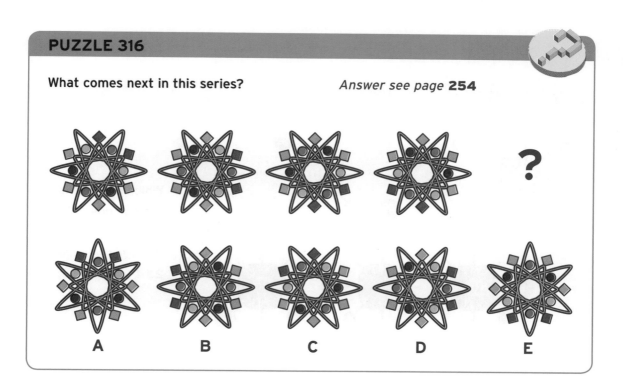

A   B   C   D   E

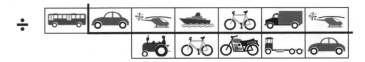

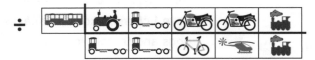

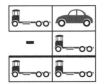 

The symbols in these calculations represent the numbers from 0 to 9. Each like symbol always represents the same number. What symbol should replace the question mark?

Answer see page **254**

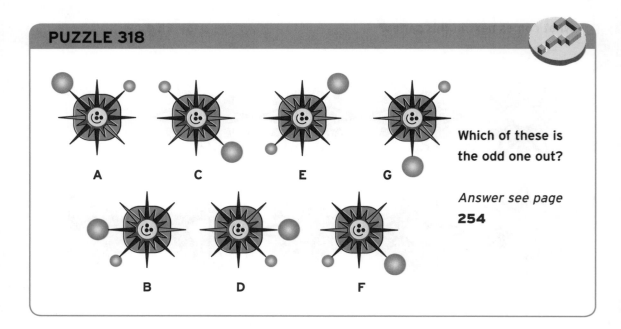

Which of these is the odd one out?

Answer see page **254**

PUZZLE 319

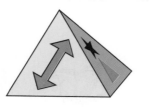

What would this pyramid look like opened out?

Answer see page **254**

A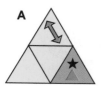

B

C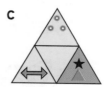

D

E

F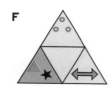

PUZZLE 320

What number replaces the question mark?

Answer see page **254**

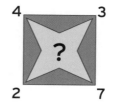

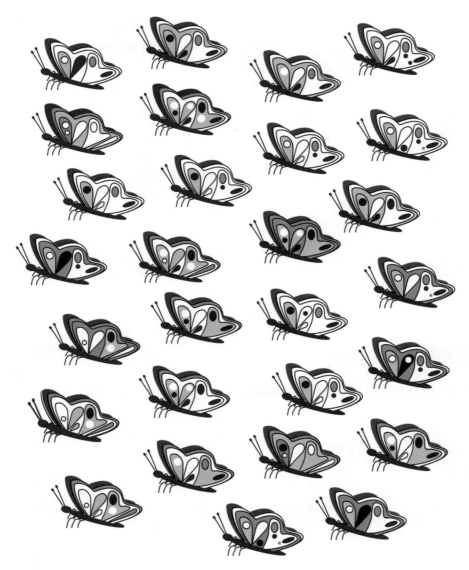

Only two of these butterflies
are identical. Which are they?

Answer see page **254**

PUZZLE 322

There is something wrong with one of the items in this set. Which one?

Answer see page **255**

A

B

C

D

E

F

PUZZLE 323

How many kangaroos are in this herd?

Answer see page **255**

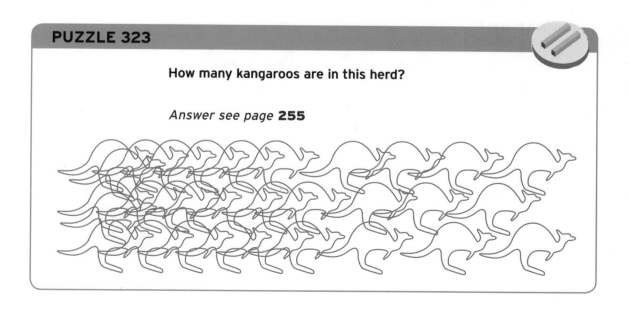

PUZZLE 324

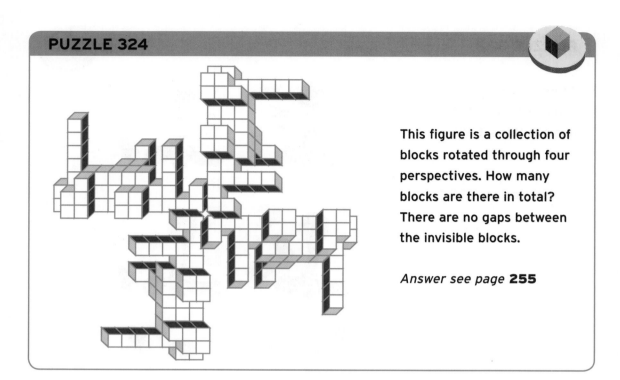

This figure is a collection of blocks rotated through four perspectives. How many blocks are there in total? There are no gaps between the invisible blocks.

Answer see page **255**

PUZZLE 325

Which pairs of letters replace the question marks?

Answer see page **255**

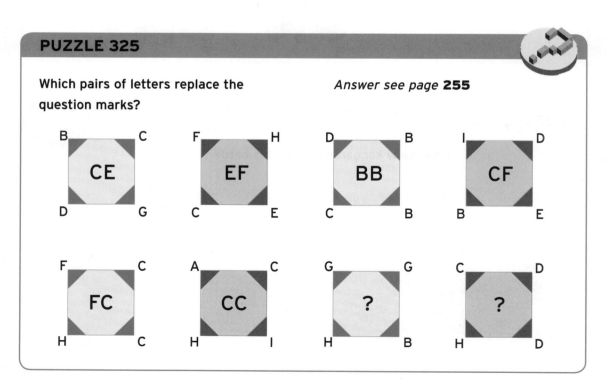

PUZZLE 326

Which of the following is the odd one out?

Answer see page **255**

A

B

C

D

PUZZLE 327

Which of the following is the odd one out?

Answer see page **255**

A

B

C

D

E

F

G

H

PUZZLE 328

$$\text{(grid 1)} - \text{(grid 2)} = \boxed{?}$$

A   B   C

D   E   F

Which panel should replace the question mark?

Answer see page 255

PUZZLE 329

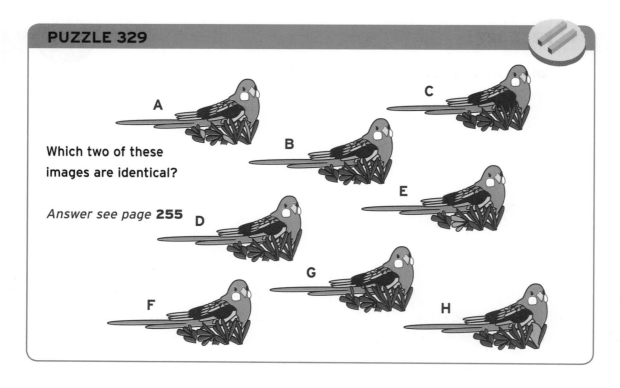

A   B   C

Which two of these images are identical?

Answer see page 255

D   E   F   G   H

PUZZLE 330

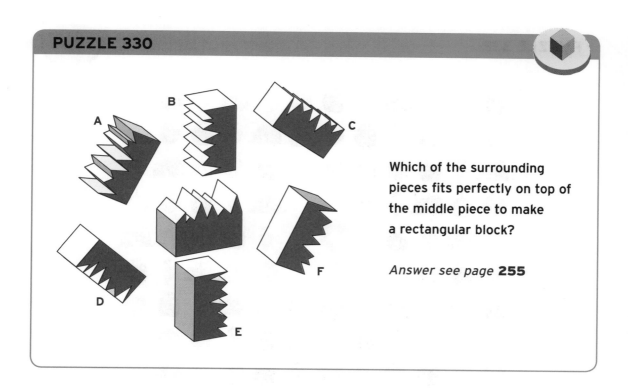

Which of the surrounding pieces fits perfectly on top of the middle piece to make a rectangular block?

Answer see page **255**

PUZZLE 331

Which of the figures below is the same as the one in the box?

Answer see page **255**

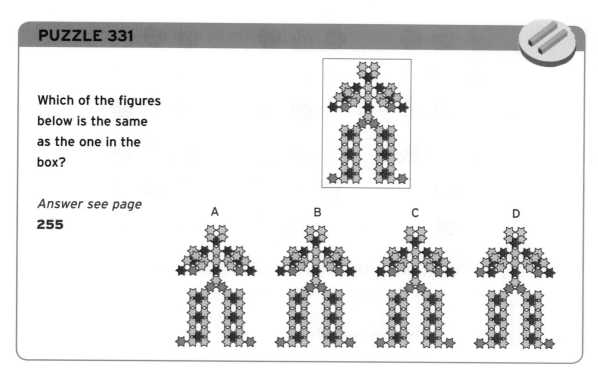

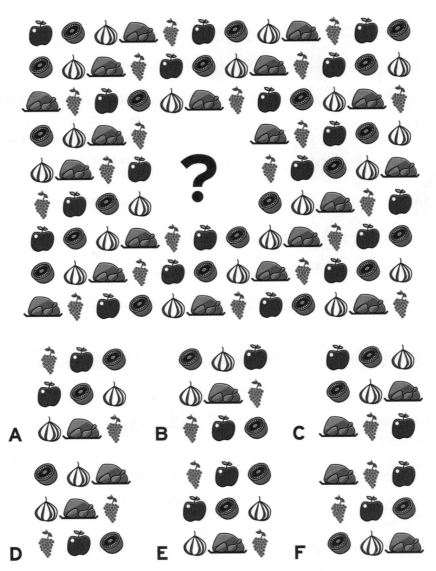

Which set should the replace the question
mark to complete the pattern?

Answer see page **255**

PUZZLE 333

Which number replaces the question mark?

Answer see page **255**

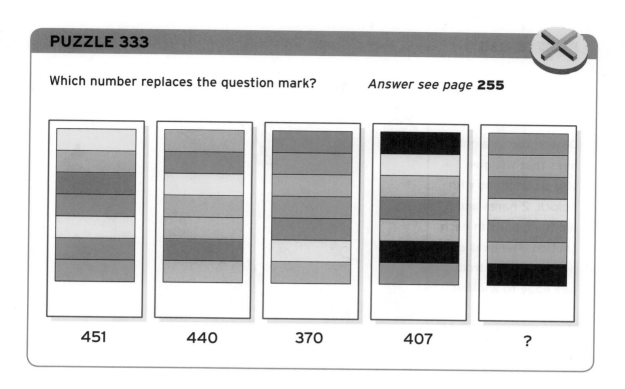

451   440   370   407   ?

PUZZLE 334

Which of the following is the odd one out?

Answer see page **255**

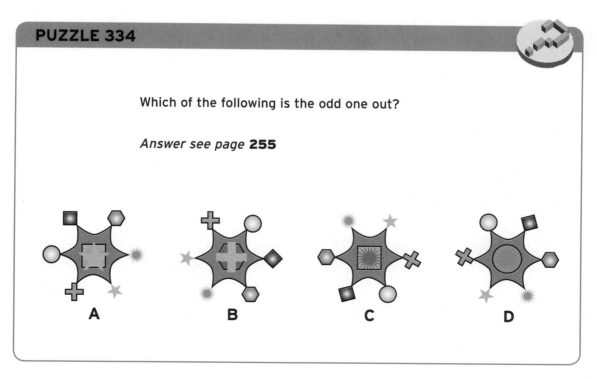

A   B   C   D

PUZZLE 335

Draw three straight lines that will give you six sections with 1 clock, 2 hares and 3 lightning bolts in each section. The lines do not have to go from one edge to another.

Answer see page **255**

PUZZLE 336

Which of these spiders and their webs make two identical pairs?

Answer see page **255**

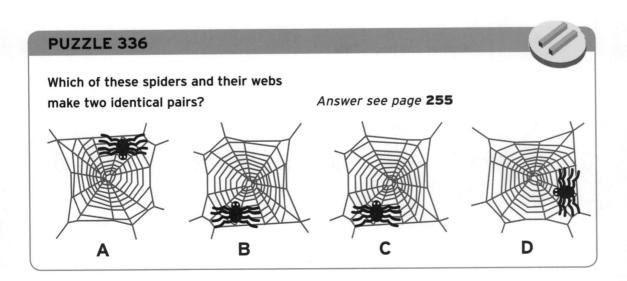

A   B   C   D

PUZZLE 337

What comes next in this series?

Answer see page **255**

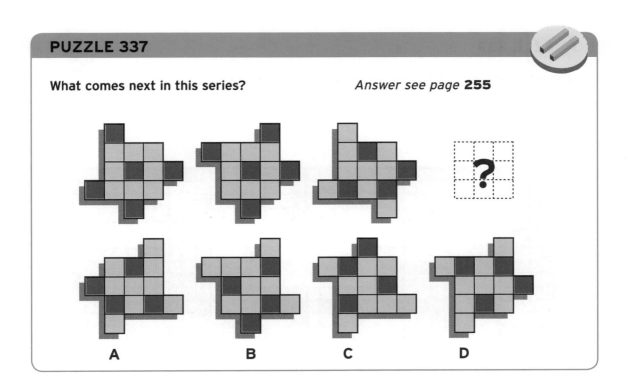

A   B   C   D

PUZZLE 338

What number replaces the question mark?

Answer see page **255**

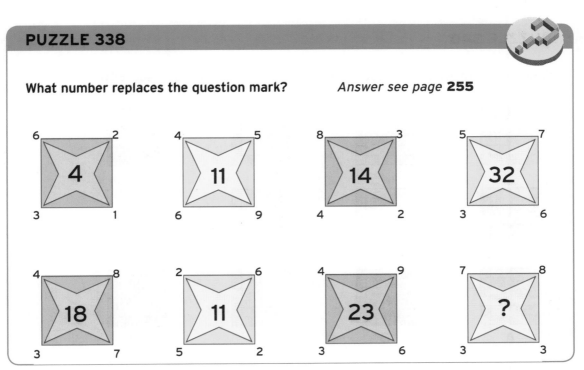

PUZZLE 339

How many yellow spotted tiles are missing from this design?

Answer see page **256**

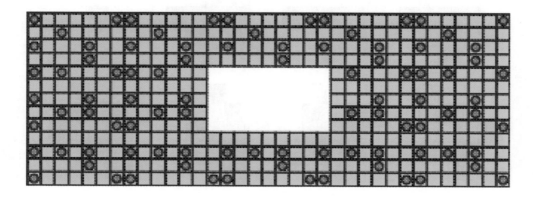

PUZZLE 340

What should replace the question mark?   *Answer see page* **256**

A   B   C   D

Which is the missing panel?   *Answer see page* **256**

A   B   C

D   E   F

PUZZLE 342

Which of the following is the odd one out?

Answer see page **256**

A   **B**   **C**   **D**

PUZZLE343

2   3   4   6   2   3   3   2   1   6   3   2
▽   ▽   ▼   ▶   ▷   ▷   △   ▲   △   ◁   ◀   ◁

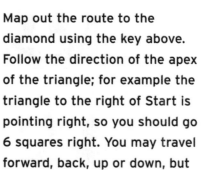

Map out the route to the diamond using the key above. Follow the direction of the apex of the triangle; for example the triangle to the right of Start is pointing right, so you should go 6 squares right. You may travel forward, back, up or down, but not diagonally nor retrace your steps, although your path may criss-cross.

Answer see page **256**

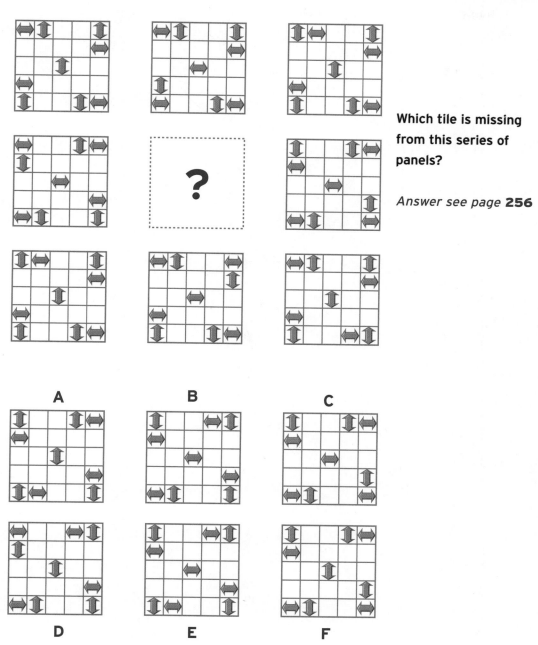

Which tile is missing from this series of panels?

Answer see page **256**

A

B

C

D

E

F

Difficult Answers

ANSWER 172

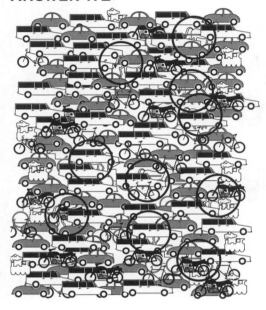

ANSWER 173

C.

ANSWER 174

A. The sequence is built according to the number of enclosed spaces in each shape.

ANSWER 175

D. Starting from the left in each row, the object rolls onto its right side with each move.

ANSWER 176

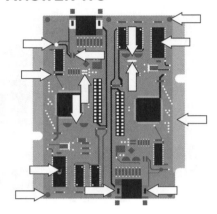

ANSWER 177

Both will fall.

ANSWER 178

B. The two sun symbols have reversed positions.

ANSWER 179

D. The others are all rotated versions of the same figure on the top half, with the mirror-images on the bottom half, but the mirror-image of D is on top.

ANSWER 180

B. The pattern rotates two sunrays one step at a time.

ANSWER 181

E. The values are:
bear = 5, horse = 1, fish = 4, bird = 3.
The sums are: 5 + 1 + 1 [7] = 4 + 3 [7];
3 + 3 [6] = 5 + 1 [6]; (4 – 1) [3] + 1 [4] =

3 + 1 [4]. The column is 4 + 5 + 3 [12 or fish + fish + fish].

ANSWER 182

A does not move, B will drop.

ANSWER 183

B. The sequence always adds two double-curved lines onto the end of the previous pattern, at the end of the last new point added.

ANSWER 184

G. The line shown in black is missing.

ANSWER 185

A. In all the others there are two pairs of two objects that touch each other.

ANSWER 186

D. The inner shapes rotate anti-clockwise; the outer shapes rotate clockwise.

ANSWER 187

D. Not all the shapes intersect.

ANSWER 188

C and H. Both have one more orange spot and one less purple spot.

ANSWER 189

B. The set is turned onto its left side and reflected horizontally.

ANSWER 190

C. Various blocks have been displaced in relation to the other shapes.

ANSWER 191

The missing symbol is G, the unladen truck (worth 0).

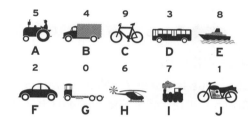

ANSWER 192

C.

ANSWER 193

It will rise.

ANSWER 194

D. In the other sets the single green spot is in the reflection of the point of intersection of the two black lines.

ANSWER 195

A.

ANSWER 196

D and G. The line in black is missing from both.

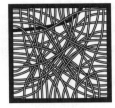

ANSWER 197

C. The bicycle (worth 0) is missing.

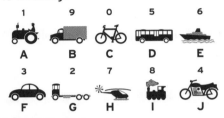

ANSWER 198

256. Blue is worth 7, Yellow 6, Red 5, Green 4, Orange 3. The numbers in each square are multiplied.

ANSWER 199

Both will rise.

ANSWER 200

A and E. B, C and D are rotated images of each other.

ANSWER 201

The symbol is based on the number of shapes it appears in. For instance, the cone (bottom right) appears in two shapes, and the tube is in three.

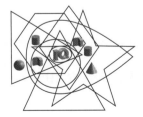

ANSWER 202

A.

ANSWER 203

A. The analogous pattern is simply upside down.

ANSWER 204

C. The pattern is made from continuously repeating the top row of tiles, rolling over two tiles with each row.

ANSWER 205

F. All the others have one or more difference.

ANSWER 206

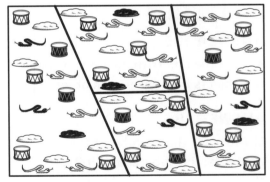

ANSWER 207

A & F, B & C, D & E.

ANSWER 208

B. Billy's plot has the greatest perimeter.

DIFFICULT ANSWERS

ANSWER 209

116. The colours are worth Yellow 8, Green 6, Orange 3, Pink 2. The halves of each square are multiplied.

ANSWER 210

They will move apart.

ANSWER 211

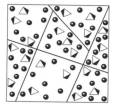

ANSWER 212

A.

ANSWER 213

H. The red columns of stars move to the right, as a pair, one column at a time; when a black column reaches the right edge, it returns to the left edge in the next set.

ANSWER 214

It will rise.

ANSWER 215

F. The figure has no eyebrows.

ANSWER 216

See picture, right.

ANSWER 217

CF. In an Orange square add 5, in a Blue one add 6.

ANSWER 218

C. The lightning bolt and pointer shape have changed place at the bottom.

ANSWER 219

D.

ANSWER 220

79. Green is worth 2, Red 3, Yellow 4, Blue 5, Orange 6. the halves of each square are added.

ANSWER 221

D. The arrow has come to the front of the objects below it.

ANSWER 222

E. The objects are rotating around the pole in a clockwise direction; the arrow must move next to make room for the cross to come round.

ANSWER 223

D.

ANSWER 224

A will rise, B will drop.

ANSWER 225

C.

DIFFICULT ANSWERS

ANSWER 226

B. There are 3 changes.

ANSWER 227

A. The lightning bolt flips upside down and changes side, as in the analogous figure.

ANSWER 228

A will rise, B will fall.

ANSWER 229

D. One of the balls has been displaced relative to the other sets, which are all rotated versions of the same set.

ANSWER 230

B. This is a mirror image of the other shapes, which are all rotated versions of the same object.

ANSWER 231

(a). They will reach the ground together (although they will be much further apart). As soon as the projectile is fired it is subject to gravity, and will approach the ground at the same downward speed as the brick, despite its forward motion.

ANSWER 232

C. The figure flips onto its right side.

ANSWER 233

B. The spots rotate clockwise one-fifth of a turn (72°) each time.

ANSWER 234

C. The same seven objects are repeated continuously in each line, regardless of tone.

ANSWER 235

F. The analogy is for two items to turn 180°, without shifting their position within the set.

ANSWER 236

D.

ANSWER 237

D. The shape is turned on its right side and the shading is reversed.

ANSWER 238

B. The purple balls are mirror-reversed.

ANSWER 239

C and E. They are mirror images. The others are the same shape in different rotations.

ANSWER 240

See pic, right.

ANSWER 241

H.

248

ANSWER 242

Here is proof that it can be done..

ANSWER 243

D. The others all go clockwise.

ANSWER 244

It will fall.

ANSWER 245

B. It is a mirror image of the others.

ANSWER 246

A will fall, B will move to the left.

ANSWER 247

C. The penguin's bill is slightly more open.

ANSWER 248

C.

ANSWER 249

14. The numbers are added. In a Pink square 5 is added, in a Green one 5 is subtracted.

ANSWER 250

B. The sequence of arrows rotates anti-clockwise, and the diamond shape in the middle is the same shading as the arrow at the top.

ANSWER 251

B.

ANSWER 252

D. The shape rotates one-eighth of a turn (45°) each time, but the leftmost star should be stacked below the one diagonally down to the right.

ANSWER 253

See picture, right.

ANSWER 254

B. There is a block missing.

ANSWER 255

B.

ANSWER 256

E. Fire is extinguished by a fire extinguisher as dirt is removed by a vacuum cleaner.

ANSWER 257

C. The pattern rotates anti- (counter) clockwise, one tenth of a turn (36°) each step.

ANSWER 258

C. Any cross in the middle three vertical tiles is always in the middle column, and the blue spot is always in the same vertical column as in the tiles to the left and right of it.

ANSWER 259

A.

ANSWER 260

A. This is a rotated mirror-image of the other shapes.

ANSWER 261

B. This is a mirror-image of the others.

ANSWER 262

C. The rectangle has moved diagonally.

ANSWER 263

B. Some of the purple diamonds have moved.

ANSWER 264

B. The balls on the diamond have switched places.

ANSWER 265

157 bricks.

ANSWER 266

A.

ANSWER 267

C. This is a rotated mirror-image of the others.

ANSWER 268

C. Each two halves of the analogy, when put together, make a complete 5 x 5 square.

ANSWER 269

E. The jet fighter is rolling to the left one fifth of a turn per step.

ANSWER 270

A. The values are: leopard = 2; flea = 3; dog = 5; rabbit = 4.

ANSWER 271

D.

ANSWER 272

D. The others are 90° rotations of the same pattern.

ANSWER 273

C. The internal configuration has changed hand in this shape.

ANSWER 274

C. The tree has an extra inner shape.

ANSWER 275

B. All the others have the same inner and outer shape.

ANSWER 276

C. When the black arrows point down, the sequence begins with a black arrow.

ANSWER 277

Follow this string:

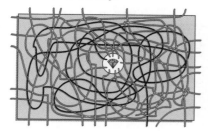

ANSWER 278

17 rattlesnakes can be collected if you follow this route:

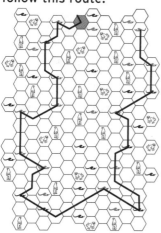

ANSWER 279

A and J. The loops have been distorted with respect to the others.

ANSWER 280

D.

ANSWER 281

B. The separate shaded cell is always one cell away from the group of three, and, if a corner group, is on the same vertical or horizontal line as the innermost cell of the group of three.

ANSWER 282

D. The tick is grey.

ANSWER 283

The differences are:

ANSWER 284

89 (based on alphanumeric values added).

ANSWER 285

C. It is a mirror image.

ANSWER 286

D. The bottom pink spot has changed place with the green spot now on its left.

ANSWER 287

B and C.

ANSWER 288

D.

ANSWER 289

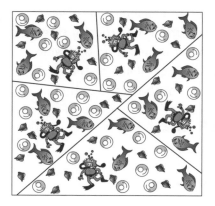

ANSWER 290

39 cobras.

ANSWER 291

B and F. In all others, the yellow circle is inside the smallest outer shape.

ANSWER 292

C. The larger shape is condensed, the whole figure is horizontally and vertically flipped and the shading changes, respectively, from black to white, white to shaded, shaded to black and black/white to white/black.

ANSWER 293

49. The colours are worth Pink 3, Green 5, Orange 12, Yellow 15. In the top row the colours are added, in the second they are divided, in the third they are subtracted, and in the fourth they are multiplied.

ANSWER 294

Follow the black route

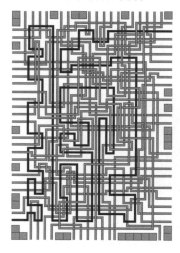

ANSWER 295

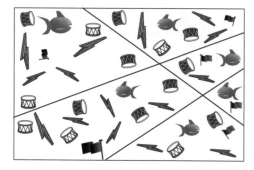

ANSWER 296

H. The inner squares have swapped shading; the bottom row is the top row taken as a whole and flipped upside down.

ANSWER 297

13. Dove = 2; football = 3; earth = 5; spiral = 4

ANSWER 298
A. The balls move alternately.

ANSWER 299
42. The colours are worth Yellow 2, Green 4, Orange 6, Pink 8. The halves of each square are added together.

ANSWER 300
E. The shapes rotate 72° clockwise each time.

ANSWER 301
C.

ANSWER 302
E.

ANSWER 303
A. The cog and star at the bottom have changed place.

ANSWER 304
C.

ANSWER 305
B. This is a mirror-image of the other shapes.

ANSWER 306
D. The star is on the wrong side in relation to the other shapes.

ANSWER 307
A.

ANSWER 308
D.

ANSWER 309
B. The object flips onto its left side.

ANSWER 310
C. It is not a rotation of the others..

ANSWER 311
Follow the black route.

ANSWER 312

ANSWER 313

61. The colours are worth Purple 3, Green 5, Red 7, Orange 9. In the top row the colours are added, in the second row they are subtracted, in the third they are multiplied, and in the fourth they are added.

ANSWER 314

The lightning bolt and the drum rotate an equal amount clockwise and anti-(counter) clockwise. The next drums are A, C and F.

ANSWER 315

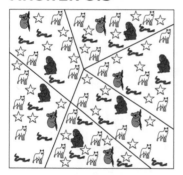

ANSWER 316

B. The objects are rotating one-sixth of a turn clockwise (60°) each step.

ANSWER 317

The helicopter (worth 2).
The symbols have the following values:

🚜	🚚	🚲	🚌	🛳
8	1	9	7	5

🚗	🚃	✳	🚂	🏍
6	3	2	0	4

$$\div\ 7\ |\ 6\ \ 2\ \ 5\ \ 9\ \ 1\ \ 2$$
$$8\ \ 9\ \ 4\ \ 1\ \ 6$$

$$\div\ 7\ |\ 8\ \ 3\ \ 4\ \ 4\ \ 0$$
$$1\ \ 1\ \ 9\ \ 2\ \ 0$$

3 6	2 0	1 2
− 3	− 8	− 2
3 3	1 2	1 0

ANSWER 318

F. In all others the small ball is diagonally opposite to the two shaded spikes.

ANSWER 319

B.

ANSWER 320

25. Multiply the numbers in opposing corners and add the products together. In a yellow square add 7, in a purple one subtract 9.

ANSWER 321

The third on the second column and the fifth on the third column.

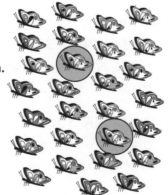

ANSWER 322

E. The white middle of the flower in this set (top right) is larger than the others.

ANSWER 323

31 kangaroos.

ANSWER 324

212 blocks (each set has 53).

ANSWER 325

GF and CH. Multiply the left numbers and add to the products of the right numbers.In a Green square add 6, in an Purple one subtract 2.

ANSWER 326

B.

ANSWER 327

D. The others are 90° rotations of the same pattern.

ANSWER 328

B.

ANSWER 329

B and F.

ANSWER 330

C.

ANSWER 331

B.

ANSWER 332

C. The series of five foods always retains the same order: apple, kiwifruit, garlic, chicken, grape.

ANSWER 333

350 (based on alphanumeric values added).

ANSWER 334

C. All the others have in the middle, an enlarged version of the objects at top-left and bottom-right.

ANSWER 335

ANSWER 336

A & B, C & D.

ANSWER 337

B. The second figure is a rotated mirror-image of the first, and so the missing figure is a similarly rotated mirror-image of the third figure.

ANSWER 338

56. Multiply top numbers and subtract

sum of bottom numbers. In an orange square subtract 4, in a Yellow one add 6.

ANSWER 339

14 spotted tiles.

ANSWER 340

B. Each object in the bottom row is a right-hand mirror-image of the shape above so, in this case, the image will be the same as the object.

ANSWER 341

A.

ANSWER 342

D. A coloured spot has changed position in the third row up.

ANSWER 343

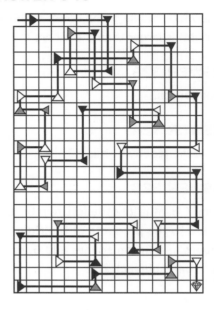

ANSWER 344

A.